Physics
by Design

with NXT MINDSTORMS
Third Edition

Revised and Expanded

Barbara Bratzel
Foreword by Chris Rogers

College House Enterprises, LLC
Knoxville, Tennessee

This textbook is intended to provide accurate and authoritative information regarding the various topics covered. It is distributed and sold with the understanding that the publisher is not engaged in providing legal, accounting, engineering or other professional services. If legal advice or other expertise advice is required, the services of a recognized professional should be retained.

Publishing and Printing Inc., Knoxville, TN printed this book from pdf files.

College House Enterprises, LLC.
5713 Glen Cove Drive
Knoxville, TN 37919, U. S. A.
Phone and/or FAX (865) 947 6174
Email jwd@collegehousebooks.com
http://www.collegehousebooks.com

10 Digit ISBN 0-9792581-7-0
13 Digit ISBN-978-0-9792581-7-6

Foreword

Update for the Mindstorms Edition

Ten years ago, Barbara was one of the first middle school teachers to embrace the Mindstorms toolset as a teaching tool, resulting in the first edition of this book. Over those ten years, teachers from every continent have started to see robotics and engineering as a powerful motivator for learning. Many have used it to teach "soft" or "life" skills as well as the more conventional academic skills. In her latest edition, Barbara kept much of her previous approach, including checklists for student learning, adapting everything for the recently released NXT Mindstorms platform. She continued to expand on her work, adding more physics and math-based activities and using the new data-logging software. With the new hardware and software, teachers should find it easier to get started in the classroom.

Foreword to the First Edition

When I first saw the prototype of what was to become the RCX, the heart of the LEGO Mindstorms product, it seemed to have an infinite number of possibilities in the classroom. It could take measurements for you; it could control motors, animate constructions, and even talk to another RCX. It seemed to me to be an ideal teaching tool to bring engineering into the pre-college classroom. What was missing is the binder of 50 different experiments for the teacher to use. When the RCX did come out, teachers embraced it, using it to infuse robotics and construction into the curriculum. They came up with many different ways of using it, from after school programs for pre-teens to kindergarten robotics, although most of the published activities were about robotics and vehicles. What is missing is using the RCX as a tool to teach other subjects and that is where this book comes in. It is the physics chapter of that binder. With this book, I hope that teachers will move beyond the robotic animals, cars, and houses and really look at teaching other content through engineering.

Barbara was an integral part of the original ROBOLAB design team as an expert "end user." She tested out different ideas on her middle school students until finally in 1998 she decided to offer a new class, "Physics by Design." This elective class would be dedicated to letting the students design and build their own experiments using the LEGO bricks as the toolset. The idea was to teach the students how to question, experiment, and answer. In the first year the class was completely oversold and students had to participate in a lottery to get in. Interestingly, the course continues to be filled to capacity despite having a second section, and also has had a strong female contingent, not commonly seen in middle school physics classrooms. Although most of this popularity is due to Barbara's teaching ability, I think the draw of designing and building (engineering) attracts students because they can see the application, they can use their hands, and actively participate in their learning.

In the era of standardized testing, I think we are losing sight of the main goal of education in my mind—to teach students how to learn on their own. We need to teach students how to be curious and ask a question, how to frame the question, how to research the question, how to validate their answer to the question, and how to communicate that answer to others. This has little to do with the content and a lot to do with the approach. Courses like Barbara's are getting harder to execute because they take longer to cover the topics than does the comparable lecture/memorization course. Standardized tests cannot test learning how to work on a team effectively, learning how to research, and learning how to plan and execute an experiment, yet all of these are, in my opinion, far more important than memorizing scientific fact. With this book, I hope that more teachers will be able to move from memorization and lecturer to investigation and mentor. There is nothing more rewarding than having a group of middle school students come back to the classroom during recess so that they can further investigate the complexities of torque or energy transfer (a common occurrence in Barbara's class). That is when you know things are going right. Students (of all ages) should be excited to go to school and learn—Barbara has accomplished this and does an excellent job of presenting these ideas in this book. I hope this is the first of many such books from outstanding teachers around the country that emphasize design over memorization. I hope you enjoy taking this into the classroom as much as I have.

Chris Rogers

Preface to the Mindstorms Edition

LEGO® robotics continues to change and grow. This third edition of Physics by Design uses both different hardware and software than the original book, which was written for the RCX and ROBOLAB. However, I hope that the spirit remains the same.

More that a decade of teaching Physics by Design has made me more certain than ever that engineering is a powerful tool in K-12 education, one that teaches critical thinking and a deeper understanding of mathematics and science concepts. More importantly, engineering gets kids excited—about science, about math, and about engineering itself. The first students who took Physics by Design are now in college and beyond. It gives me special pleasure that a number of them have gone on to pursue engineering--and have told me that their LEGO physics class started them down that path.

Every year, the students in Physics by Design, an eighth-grade science class at the Shady Hill School in Cambridge Massachusetts, design their own pan balances using LEGO pieces, string, and a set of metric masses. The design is left to them. The only requirement is that the finished balance must be accurate to within 0.5 grams. The students design and build, test and modify, until they are satisfied with their balances. When they decide they are ready, they put their balances to the final test—determining the mass of four unknown objects.

These students are doing engineering while at the same time applying what they have learned about center of gravity, stability, and torque. Using the concepts in an actual design project reinforces them more effectively than completing any number of problem sets. In addition, the students have fun building their balances and feel a considerable sense of accomplishment when they successfully complete the challenge.

Physics by Design is a project-based course that teaches classical mechanics through engineering. It covers motion, forces, fluids, stability, work, and energy. The topics are approached from an engineering perspective, with building and designing reinforcing the conceptual physics material and vice versa. Most of the designing and building is done using LEGO bricks, including the Mindstorms NXT. All of the students in the course learn programming as well as physics; by the end of the year, they are adept at it.

Physics by Design was inspired by the work of the Center for Engineering Education and Outreach at Tufts University. The CEEO is dedicated to bringing engineering into the K-12 classroom. They have had great success in integrating engineering into math and science classes, as well as reading, writing, social studies, and art classes, in schools around the world. I have been lucky enough to work with Professor Chris Rogers and the staff and students at the Center for a number of years.

Physics by Design is the most rewarding course I have ever taught. I love seeing the pride that the students feel when they are successful in solving problems and the confidence they gain through the year as they tackle harder design challenges. I love the delight that students feel when they discover a talent for engineering or programming that they never suspected they had. I love that the course lets me be a mentor and a coach, rather than a lecturer and a director.

I hope that this book will help other teachers incorporate engineering into their science courses.

Acknowledgements

Many people helped create the Physics by Design course and this book. Most of all, I want to thank all of the Physics by Design students, whose insight, creativity, and humor have made the course such a joy to teach and whose feedback strengthened it considerably. Dylan Morris and Shinjini Mukherjee returned years after taking the course to help teach it. Moussou N'Diaye, along with my daughters Audrey and Nell, provided valuable feedback about the activities.

I am deeply indebted to Chris Rogers, without whom the course would not have been possible. He first introduced me to the idea of teaching science through engineering many years ago and he has been a constant source of inspiration, assistance, and infectious enthusiasm ever since.

I am grateful for all of the ideas and help I have gotten from the people at the Center for Engineering Education and Outreach, in particular Adam Carberry, Martha Cyr, Brian Gravel, Elissa Milto, Merredith Portsmore, Robert Rasmussen, and Kevin Staszowski; and from the members of the science department at Shady Hill: Monica Chrambach, Michael Horn, Jeanne McDermott, and especially Tracy Polte, who enriched Physics by Design during the year she taught it and who cheerfully shares a room with me and all of the LEGO® bricks. Thank you also to Cathy Helgoe, who edited the activities I wrote for the LEGO Invent and Investigate database (some of which I modified for Physics by Design) and Dan LaFountain, who taught the original LEGO workshop that got me so excited. Many teachers, in particular Andrew Hart and Bernard Catt in Australia, have offered valuable suggestions for the book.

Jim Dally, who edited and published this book, improved it immeasurably with his many thoughtful suggestions. Finally, this book would not have been possible without the patience and support of my husband, Jacob, and daughters, Audrey and Nell.

Table of Contents

Foreword
Preface to the Mindstorms Edition
Acknowledgements

Part Five: Projects

Part Six: Data Logging Activities

Part Seven: Physics Activities

Part Eight: Mostly Mathematics Activities

Appendix A: Alignment with the National Science Standards
Appendix B: Activities Listed by Topic
Appendix C: Mindstorms Equipment Used for Each Activity

Part One: Getting Started

About this Book

Physics by Design has eight parts. The first section gives tips for managing the class and the materials. Part Two contains introductory activities for the NXT, including instructions for building simple cars. Part Three is a series of tutorials for teaching Common-Palette programming to a whole class with just one teacher. The structure of the tutorials lets the students work at their own pace and enables the teacher to concentrate on helping those students who need the most support. Part Four covers the Complete Palette in the same way. The fifth section contains projects that allow the students to apply the programming and building skills that they have learned to more open-ended and creative challenges. Part Six introduces the students to data logging using NXT Mindstorms. The final two sections contain activities for teaching physics and mathematics using LEGO® bricks and NXT Mindstorms.

Most of the activities in this book use Mindstorms equipment: NXTs, motors, lamp bricks, and sensors. There are a number of activities in the Physics section that require only LEGO bricks and other non-Mindstorms materials. The Mindstorms equipment needed for each activity, if any, is summarized in Appendix C.

The activities in this book were written for NXT Mindstorms 2.0. If you are using an earlier version, you will not be able to do the data-logging activities.

Classroom Management

Project Rules

I begin the year by distributing and discussing a set of project rules. The rules are included at the end of this chapter. I find that enforcing these behavior guidelines improves the tone in the classroom considerably.

Encouraging Help

From the first day of class, I encourage the students to collaborate and to help one another. No designs are secret—the students are welcome to incorporate good ideas from other groups into their projects. I stress that having another group adopt one's idea is a real compliment.

If someone finds a clever solution to a problem, I make that person the "expert" on that issue and send other students with similar problems to talk to him or her. If students are having a good deal of difficulty with a project and seem stuck, I encourage them to "go shopping," to wander around the class and look at everyone else's projects to see how others have tackled the problem.

I find that if I consistently give positive feedback to students who help one another, then soon the class culture becomes one of helping. The students no longer look to me as the only source of advice; instead, they consult one another. Aside from making the atmosphere of the class more pleasant, doing this means that I can supervise a whole class without being run ragged or having the students spend long periods of time waiting for help.

Competition

As part of my class, I run competitions all the time. However, I almost never have the students compete directly against one another. If a competition has a clear winner, it also has a room full of losers—not a cheerful prospect. Instead, I have the students compete against a set standard; for example, can your bug stay inside the box for thirty seconds. That way, the potential is there for the entire class to win. Also, with this kind of competition, there is no penalty for aiding others or sharing a good idea—helping another group succeed does not diminish your own group's prospects.

Failure

In a project-based class, failure is inevitable. An idea that seems good at first turns out to be a dead-end—or an outright disaster. As the upset students sit amid the ruins of their project, I praise them for taking a risk and point out the positive aspects of their plan. I help them see what they have learned about which designs do and don't work. I remind them that everyone in the class will have a design fail at some point in the year. I also make sure that they get no jeering or other negative response from the other students.

Appealing to Girls

Over the years, I have tried hard to make the course appealing to girls. The effort has been successful; girls and boys sign up for the course in roughly equal numbers.

One important lesson I have learned is that girls do not like cars. Announce a project involving cars and the boys perk up while the girls' eyes glaze over. Because of this, I limit the number of projects I do involving cars, even though cars are a natural use of the NXT. Instead, I make fans, snails, music boxes—projects that cover the same concepts but avoid cars.

Girls, in general, do not like direct competition as much as boys do. Instead of having the students compete against one another, I have them compete against a set standard. (See the section on competition, above.)

Girls tend to plan ahead more than boys. When I announce a new project, the girls grab a piece of paper and start sketching their ideas. The boys, on the other hand, head for the bins of LEGO® materials to collect every piece they think they might need, then worry abut what they are going to do with them. To accommodate both styles, I have accumulated a lot of LEGO materials. When the girls finish planning and go to gather their materials, there are still plenty of choice LEGO pieces left.

I tend to pair girls with girls and boys with boys, especially at the beginning of the year. I have found that mixed-genders pairs sometimes struggle to work together smoothly, much more so than in traditional science courses. The biggest complaint: the girls say that the boys take over the building projects.

One last note: color matters. Girls tend not to like the stark white-and-gray color scheme of the NXT as much as boys do. In fact, I find that the girls generally notice color more than the boys do. Girls are much more likely to plan a color scheme for their projects. I make sure that my LEGO® brick collection contains the full range of colors—purple, orange, pastels- as well as the traditional LEGO brick colors.

Builders vs. Programmers

Many of the students quickly find one aspect of the projects, either the building or the programming, more appealing than the other and start to specialize. I allow this to some extent, while stressing that everyone needs to become competent at both. To ensure that they do, I give periodic building quizzes and programming quizzes. Neither one is particularly difficult; instead, each is designed to test whether the students have mastered the basics.

Materials Management

Computer Equipment

The ideal equipment for a class like this is one computer and NXT per group. Though the initial cost is substantial, the equipment can be used year after year. If one computer per group is not available, it is possible to do many of the projects with groups sharing computers. However, projects that require a lot of computer time are difficult.

Another useful item is a projector that can be hooked up to a computer. With a projector, the entire class can view and discuss a Mindstorms program at once. This option is especially valuable for introducing new programming techniques and for viewing class data from experiments.

LEGO® Materials

Each pair of students in my class has an assigned NXT Mindstorms set. In addition, the students can help themselves to extra LEGO materials from my collection. I have a bin for each type of LEGO piece—bricks, plates, wheels, gears and pulleys, etc.

My goal is never to have the availability of materials limit the student's ideas. After a number of years of teaching the course, I am near to this goal. Each year, I use my budget money to buy more of whichever pieces have been in short supply during the preceding year. However, some items, such as gears or wheels, can be a limiting factor. At the start of a project, I announce those limits to the group. For example, I might tell them that each group may only use two large wheels for the project.

I also have a labeled bin for each student group. The students store their projects in their bins between classes.

Additional Resources

Online:
LEGOengineering. http://www.legoengineering.com/. A comprehensive website for teaching engineering with LEGO® materials, including the NXT. The site includes lesson plans, information about upcoming conferences, downloadable programs, and many other useful features.

The Tufts University Center for Engineering Education and Outreach. http://ceeo.tufts.edu/. An excellent website for all aspects of teaching engineering, from research to curriculum to workshops.

LEGO Mindstorms Education. http://www.lego.com/eng/education/mindstorms/. The official Mindstorms Education site with detailed information about using (and of course buying) LEGO products.

Books:
LEGO NXT for ROBOLAB Users: Migrating from the RCX to the NXT by Eric L. Wang. An engaging and thorough introduction to NXT Mindstorms, geared towards ROBOLAB users, but useful for anyone new to the NXT.

Physics with Robotics: An NXT and RCX Activity Guide for Secondary and College Physics by William Church, Tony Ford, and Natasha Perova. Robotics activities for high-school and college physics classes, many of which could be adapted for the middle-school classroom.

Classroom Activities for the Busy Teacher: NXT by Damien Kee. Ready-to-use lesson plans for the NXT.

Brick Layers II: Creative Engineering with LEGO Constructions by the AIMS Education Foundation. A non-Mindstorms reference book full of creative and well-planned engineering projects using LEGO materials, most involving simple machines.

Project Rules

We will be doing projects, both large and small, throughout the year. Sometimes your attempt will be a success. Other times, it will be a miserable failure. Either result is okay—failure is an integral part of the design process.

What is not okay: laughing at someone else's project.

So, some rules for working in the class:

1. You may not criticize or make fun of anther student's work. This includes laughing, teasing, or comparisons ("My car is so much better than your car....").
2. However, you may provide CONSTRUCTIVE criticism. To be constructive, the comment must be specific and offer a possible solution. For example, "Hey your car doesn't go straight" is not acceptable, but "I noticed that your car veers to the left. It looks like the back wheel is rubbing against the frame" is welcomed.
3. No designs are private property. Anyone may get ideas from any other design. If someone copies a piece of your design, the proper reaction is to be flattered—clearly, the other person has recognized your brilliance.
4. If you get stuck, feel free to look at other people's designs to see how they have solved similar problems.
5. And finally, relax! Things will go wrong—but you will have plenty of time and assistance to fix the problems.

Part Two: Introductory Activities

This set of activities introduces the NXT and the Mindstorms software.

The activities in this section are:
1. Build a Box
2. Picture Box
3. Simple Two-Motor Car I
4. Simple Two-Motor Car II

The first activity, Build a Box, introduces the students to the beam-and-peg building system that is the basis of NXT designs. In Picture Box, the students improve upon this box by writing a simple program to add a picture to its floor. The last two activities are building plans for simple cars. The students can build these cars as an introductory activity or refer to the plans as they build cars in later activities.

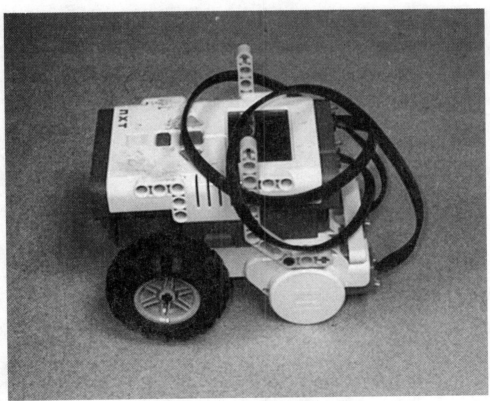

A simple two-motor NXT car.

Build a Box

Build a box to hold the red and blue balls. The box must use the NXT as its base and must have a hinged lid for placing and removing the balls.

Here are some helpful hints:

Connector pegs can be used to attach a beam to the NXT. If a single peg is used, then the beam will be able to swing back and forth (a hinge!). If two or more pegs are used, the beam will be held in a fixed position.

Beams with studs may be attached at right angles to one another by placing the studs of one beam into the holes of the other. Beams may also be attached at right angles with connector pegs. To make the holes on the horizontal beams line up with the vertical beam, place two plates between the horizontal beams.

Extra: If you have time, design a latch for your lid so that it can be fastened shut.

1. What was the easiest aspect of building the box?

2. What was most difficult?

3. Make a sketch of your hinge.

Teacher Information   Build a Box

This introductory activity allows the students to become familiar with the beam-and-peg building system and to learn how to attach beams to the NXT.

An NXT box with its hinged lid open.

Objectives
1. To gain comfort in building using beams and pegs.
2. To learn ways of attaching beams to the NXT.
3. To devise methods of forming right angles using beams and pegs.
4. To engage in creative problem solving.

Materials
NXT
LEGO® pieces
Red and blue balls

Time: Approximately 40 minutes

Notes
1. Stress that there are many possible solutions to this problem. At the end of the activity, have the students share some of their favorite ideas with the rest of the class.
2. You may want to demonstrate the difference between friction and non-friction connector pegs.
3. You may want to demonstrate how to attach beams at right angles using connector pegs. To make the holes on the horizontal beams line up with the vertical beam, place two plates between the horizontal beams.

Answers to Build a Box

1. Answers will vary.
2. Answers will vary. Common answers are designing the hinge or figuring out how to attach beams to the NXT.
3. Answers will vary.

Picture Box

Open the Mindstorms NXT software. Start a new program by highlighting "Untitled-1" under Start New Program.

Type in "Picture Box." Then click on Go. A blank grid will open. This is where you will write your program. Click on the green circle in the lower left corner. The word Common should appear, followed by a column of icons. You will drag and drop these icons to write your program.

The fourth icon in the column is a Display block ⬛. Click on it and drag it onto the grid next to the orange starting point for the program. Drop the Display block. The beam should connect to it and the Display block should no longer be grayed out. Click on the block. Below the grid, you will see information about this block.

In the File section, you will see a menu of possible pictures. As you click on the name of a picture, its image will appear to the right. Choose the picture you want to appear on the floor of your box.

Next, click on the hourglass icon in the column. Select the Wait for Time block and add it to your program. Set the time for ten seconds.

Connect the NXT to the computer using the USB cord. Download your program to the NXT and run it by pressing the Download and Run arrow ▶ in the lower right corner of the computer screen.

Teacher Information

Picture Box

This activity introduces the students to the Mindstorms NXT software with a simple two-step program.

Objectives
1. To learn how to open the Mindstorms software and write a simple program.
2. To download and run a program.

Materials
NXT box from the previous activity
Computer

Time: Approximately 20 minutes

Notes
1. You may want to demonstrate how to create and download a program before beginning this activity.

Sample Program for Picture Box

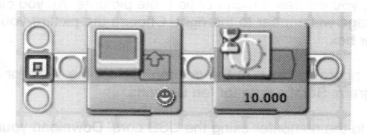

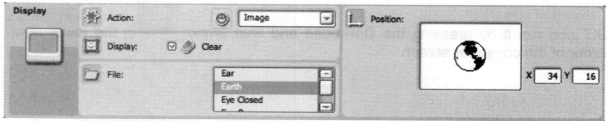

This program displays a picture of Earth on the bottom of the box.

Simple Two-Motor Car I

Simple car I. This model is made with the rechargeable battery pack. Disposable batteries may be used instead.

A top view of the car.

A side view of the car.

The design of the front slider.

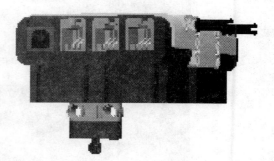

Two views of the car showing the placement of the front slider and side connector pegs.

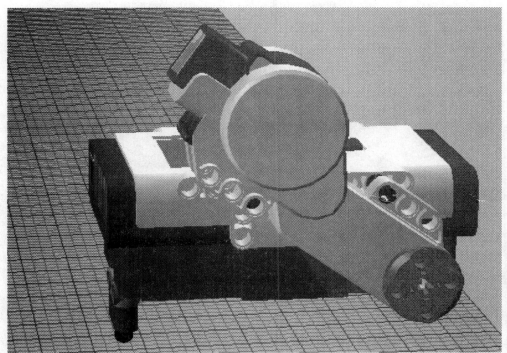

Each motor is mounted at an angle using two connector pegs.

A studless beam connects the two motors.

A number of different sliders or wheels can be used on the front of the car. Some possibilities are shown below.

Possible front ends. Top row: caster wheel, fixed wheel. Bottom row: sliders.

Simple Two-Motor Car II

A simple two-motor car. The car uses only two wheels, directly connected to the two motors. In lieu of a second set of wheels, the car rests on the ridged sections of the motors.

A front view of the car. The motors are connected by a single beam across the front and an axle on the bottom. (The drawings are shown without the cables, to make the pieces easier to see.)

A bottom view of the car. An axle connects the two motors. The gray ridged sections of the motors slide along the ground in place of wheels.

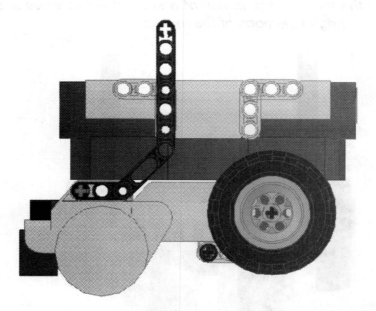

A side view of the car. Each motor is attached to the side of the NXT by a single curved beam.

The finished car, except for the cables connecting the motors to the NXT. This car works best on a smooth, hard surface. For use on other surfaces, adding a front wheel or slider will improve its performance.

This modified car has a column of beams and bricks with a skid plate at the bottom, so that the front of the car is resting on the skid plate rather than on the ridged sections of the motors.

The car modified for use with the rechargeable battery pack, rather than with disposable batteries. Since the battery pack is not flush with the bottom of the car, the side beams must be moved down one peg for use with a battery-pack car.

Teacher Information   Simple Two-Motor Cars I and II

The students learn how to build simple NXT cars.

Once the students are comfortable with the basics of building cars, they quickly go on to create their own designs.

Objectives
1. To learn how to build a two-motor NXT car.
2. To gain additional experience with beam-and peg construction.

Materials
NXT
Motors
LEGO® parts, including wheels

Time: Approximately 30 minutes

Notes
1. Building cars can be done as a stand-alone activity or as part of the Common-Palette tutorial, where cars are introduced in the Mimicry activity.

Part Three: Common Palette Activities

This set of activities introduces NXT Mindstorms programming using the Common Palette.

The activities in this section are:

1. Hello Goodbye
2. Say Cheese
3. Mimicry
4. Snake
5. Push-Button Car
6. Cloverleaf

These six activities are designed to be done as a single unit, with the students working at their own pace, receiving help from the teacher as needed. Each activity sheet contains a short program to write.

One way of organizing the class as the students learn the Common Palette is to give them Common Sense sheets to fill out as they work. When a student successfully completes an activity, he or she brings the NXT with the completed program to the teacher for inspection. The teacher approves it by stamping the student's Common Sense sheet in the appropriate box. The student is then free to progress to the next activity. Using the Common Sense sheet allows the teacher to keep track of everyone's progress while concentrating on helping those students who need the most assistance.

Some groups will probably complete Common Sense before others. Clean Sweep in the Projects section is a good follow-up activity. The programming involved follows naturally from Snake, Push-Button Motor, and Cloverleaf. The students who finish Common Sense early can spend a significant amount of time on Clean Sweep, perfecting their sweeper and practicing driving it. The other students can work on Clean Sweep for shorter periods of time. Another good culminating activity for Common Sense is Bug in a Box in the Projects section.

A quiz is included at the end of the chapter to test the students' understanding of Common-Palette programming.

Common Sense

As you complete each Common Palette programming sheet, demonstrate your program to the teacher. Make sure that you get the stamp of approval for each activity before moving on to the next one.

Hello Goodbye	
Say Cheese	
Mimicry	
Snake	
Push-Button Car	
Cloverleaf	

Hello Goodbye

Your NXT can be programmed to do all kinds of fancy and elaborate things. However, first you will have to learn the NXT Mindstorms programming language. We will go through it step by step, starting with simple programs and moving on to more complicated ones.

NXT Mindstorms has two palettes, the Common Palette and the Complete Palette. The common palette contains the more commonly used icons; we will start with it.

Start a new program by highlighting "Untitled-1" under Start New Program.

Type in "Hello Goodbye." Then click on Go. A blank grid will open. This is where you will write your program. Click on the green circle in the lower left corner. The word Common should appear, followed by a column of icons. You will drag and drop these blocks to write your program.

The third icon in the column is a Sound block . Click on it and drag it onto the grid next to the orange stating point. Drop the Sound block. The beam should connect to it and the Sound block should no longer be grayed out. Click on the Sound block. Below the grid, you will see information about this block.

Change the information so that it matches the picture below. This will program your NXT to say hello.

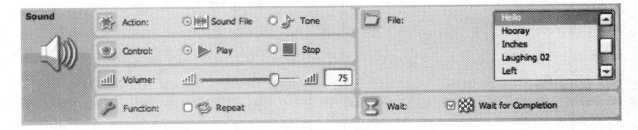

Let's try running this program. Connect your NXT to the computer using the USB cable. Turn on your NXT. Download the program to your NXT by clicking on the "Download and Run" arrow in the lower right corner of the screen. Your NXT should say hello.

Your task: Make this Hello program a bit fancier. Add two more Sound blocks to your program, after the Hello block. Program the third block to say Goodbye by clicking on it and changing the information panel below.

For the middle block, the sound is up to you. Choose a sound from the file list on the information panel.

Run your program. The NXT should say hello, make the sound you've chosen, then say goodbye.

Teacher Information

Hello Goodbye

This activity serves as an introduction to NXT Mindstorms.

Objectives
1. To be able to write a simple NXT program.
2. To learn how to download programs to the NXT.

Materials
NXT
Computer

Time: Approximately 20 minutes

Notes
1. If the students have completed the introductory activity Picture Box, they will already know how write and download a simple program. Otherwise, you may want to demonstrate these basics.
2. The volume on the NXT can be adjusted. To do so, starting at the My Files screen, press the right arrow button repeatedly until you reach Settings. Push the orange button; the screen should now say Volume. Press the orange button again and then use the right and left arrow buttons to adjust the volume. Press the orange button to select your choice and return to the Settings screen.

Sample Program for Hello Goodbye

First Sound block:

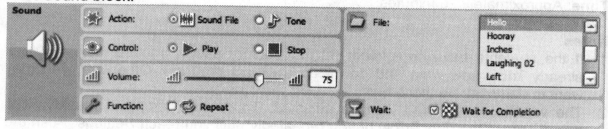

Second Sound block:

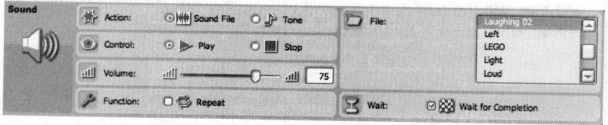

Third Sound block:

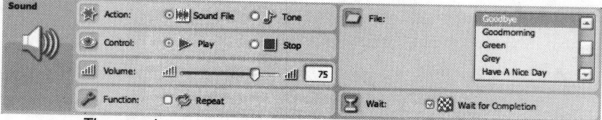

The sample program says hello, laughs, and says goodbye.

Say Cheese

In this program, you will use a sensor to trigger an action. Sometimes, photographers instruct their subjects to say cheese before snapping the picture, because saying the word "cheese" forms your mouth into a smile. Your program will respond to the spoken word "cheese" by displaying a smile face.

Plug the sound sensor into port 1 of your NXT. Start a new program and name it Say Cheese. This program will use two Display blocks (located in the middle of the icon column), one Wait for Sound block, and one Wait for Time block. The Wait blocks can be found by clicking on the hourglass icon.

Your task: Write a program that displays the words "Say Cheese" on the NXT screen, waits for the user to say the word "cheese," then displays a smile face.

To display the words "Say Cheese," add a Display block to your program. In the information section at the bottom, choose Text, and then write the words "Say Cheese" in the text box.

For the next step of your program, you will need the Wait for Sound block. Drag it to your program. In the information section, change the settings to match the ones below.

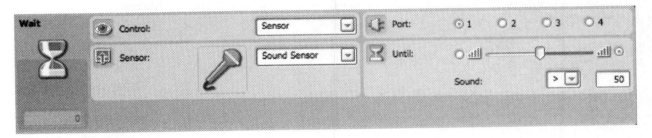

For the third step, select a second Display block. Adjust the settings to make it display a smile face on the screen. After the Display block, add a Wait for Time block and set the time to one second. If you do not include this block, you will not be able to see the smile face because the program will end immediately.

Connect the USB cord and try downloading and running your program.

Teacher Information

Say Cheese

This activity introduces the students to sensors.

Objectives
1. To be able to write simple NXT Mindstorm programs.
2. To learn to program using a sensor.

Materials
NXT
Computer
Sound sensor

Time: Approximately 20 minutes

Notes
1. You may want to demonstrate how to attach sensors to the NXT before starting the activity.
2. The volume on the NXT can be adjusted. To do so, starting at the My Files screen, press the right arrow button repeatedly until you reach Settings. Push the orange button; the screen should now say Volume. Press the orange button again and then use the right and left arrow buttons to adjust the volume. Press the orange button to select your choice and return to the Settings screen.

Sample Program for Say Cheese

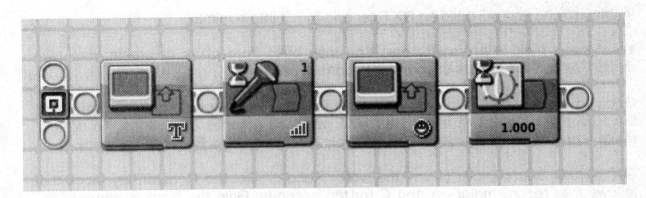

First Display block:

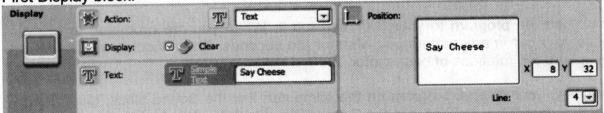

First Wait block:

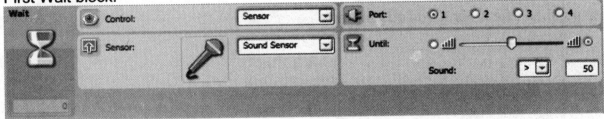

Second Display block:

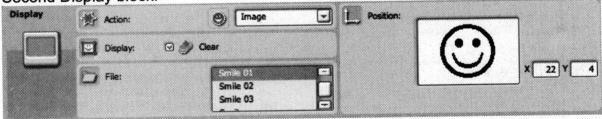

Second Wait block:

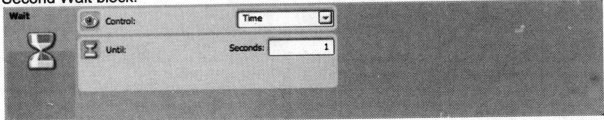

Mimicry

In this activity, you will build an NXT car and turn it into a mimic.

Your task: Build a two-motor car. You may build from plans or create your own design. Attach the motors of your car to ports A and C.

Once your car is complete, you are ready to program it. Open a new program. Use the Record/Play block to make your NXT car copy a series of motions. To do this, make a program of two blocks—a Sound block followed by a Record/Play block.

Set the first Sound block to say the word "Record." Set the Record/Play block that follows it to record motors A and C for ten seconds. Give the block a name in the indicated space.

Download the program to your NXT and run it. When you are prompted to record, move your car in any pattern you wish for ten seconds. The encoders in the motors will record the rotations of each motor.

Return to your original program on the computer. For the Sound block, change it to say the word "Play." Then, set the Record/Play block to play. Make sure that it has the same name as your original Record block.

Download and run your modified program.

Teacher Information   Mimicry

The students build a simple car and use the Record/Play block to make an NXT mimic.

Objectives
1. To build a simple two-motor NXT car.
2. To use the Record/Play block.

Materials
NXT
Motors
LEGO® pieces
Computer

Time: Approximately 50 minutes

Notes
1. To build the cars, the students can use the simple two-motor car designs in the Introductory Activities section or design their own cars.
2. You may want to demonstrate the use of the Record/Play block to the students before beginning this activity.

Sample Program for Mimicry

Record program:

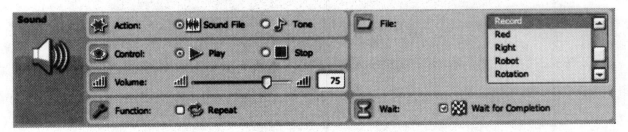

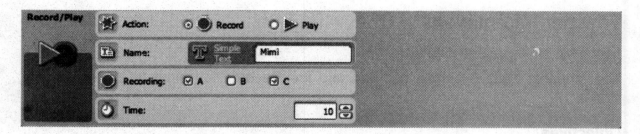

Play program:

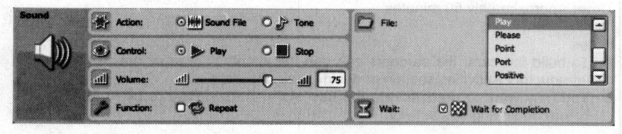

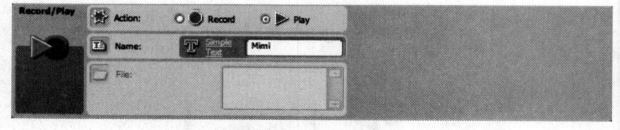

Snake

In this activity, you will write a program that makes your car move in a series of S curves, curving first in one direction and then in the other.

For this task, you will need to use a loop, a programming structure that repeats a sequence of steps over and over. In this case, your loop will contain two blocks, one to make the car curve to the left and one to make it curve to the right.

The Loop icon is the penultimate (next to last) one in the Common-Palette column. Once you drag the Loop block to the grid, it will look like this:

To add tasks to the loop, drag the appropriate block to the loop and drop it in. The loop will expand to engulf the new block. For example, to make the snake curve, you would add a Move block to the loop and move the steering bar towards one side. Remember to make sure that the ports in your program match the ports on your car.

Once you have written your program, download it to the NXT using the Download button, which is to the left and below the Download and Run button you used previously. This button downloads the program, but does not run it immediately, allowing you to disconnect the USB cord and position the NXT before starting the program.

Test your snake program. You will probably need to adjust the power, the duration, and the degree of turning to produce a snake-like motion.

Teacher Information   Snake

The students program cars to move in a snake-like pattern.

Objectives
1. To write a program that includes a loop.
2. To use the Move block to control a motor.
3. To learn the difference between Download and Download and Run.

Materials
NXT car from the previous activity
Computer

Time: Approximately 20 minutes

Notes
1. This activity uses the car that the students built for the previous activity, Mimicry. If the students need to build a car instead, any simple two-motor car works well.
2. Once the students have written and tested the basic program, have them adjust the power, duration, and degree of turning to get a satisfyingly snake-like motion.

Sample Program for Snake

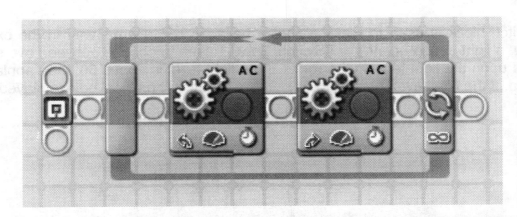

Loop

First Move block:

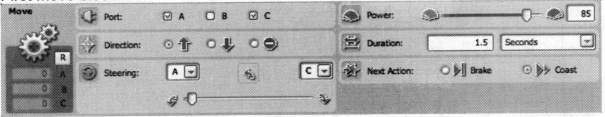

Second Move block:

Push-Button Car

A Switch block is used to make a choice between two alternatives. In the example below, a light-sensor–controlled Switch block is used to choose between two sounds based upon the light level in the room. If the light level is above 60, then applause is played. If the light level is equal to or below 60, then a C musical note is played.

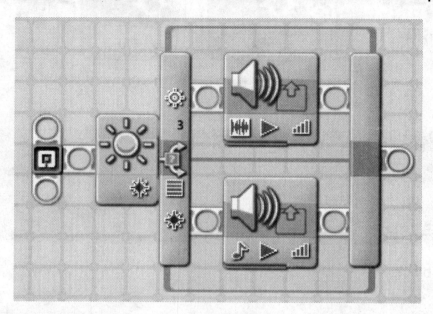

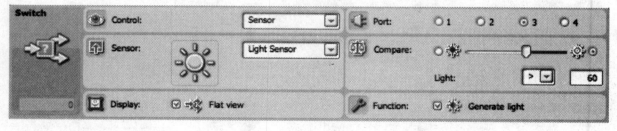

Top Sound block:

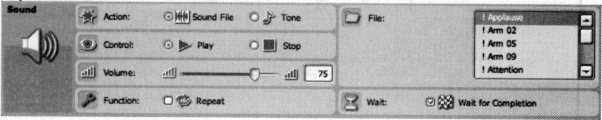

Bottom Sound block:

Study the example program above. Then, try writing a Switch-block program of your own.

Your task: Using a touch-sensor-controlled switch, write a program that turns the car's motors on while a touch sensor is depressed and off while it is released. In order to make the sequence repeat forever, you will need a loop in addition to the switch.

Teacher Information   Push-Button Car

The students learn how to use Switch blocks.

Objectives
1. To learn how to use Switch blocks.
2. To write a program containing both a loop and a switch.

Materials
NXT car from the previous activity
Computer
Touch sensor

Time
Approximately 40 minutes

Notes
1. Some students may need help in deciding how to arrange the loop and switch within their program.
2. You may want to have the students outline the program on paper before writing it on the computer.

Sample Program for Push-Button Car

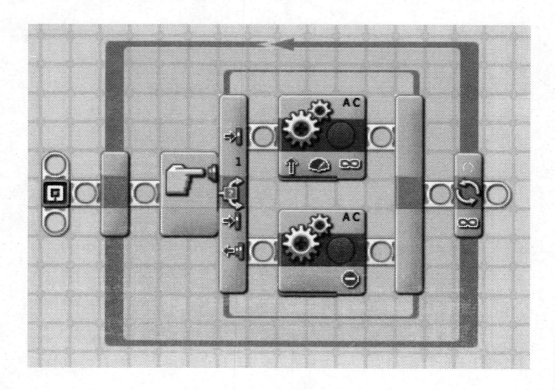

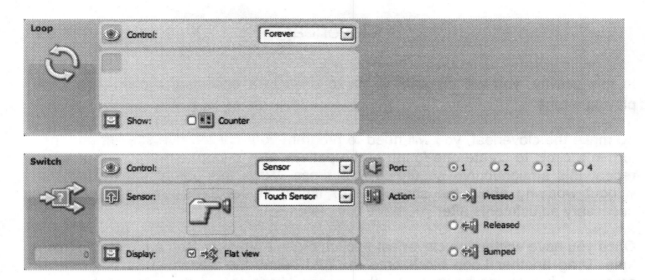

Top Move block:

Bottom Move block:

Cloverleaf

In this activity, you will program a car to drive in a cloverleaf pattern ⌘ while playing a tune.

To make the cloverleaf, you will need to program your car to drive straight and then turn in a circle to create one-fourth of the pattern. Use a loop to make your program repeat this straight/curve sequence four times. Write this portion of the program without worrying about the sharpness or timing of the turns. You will make the necessary adjustments after you have completed your program.

Once you have written the cloverleaf section of your program, you are ready to add a tune. Drag another Loop block onto the grid below the cloverleaf section of your program. Click on the beam below the orange Mindstorms icon at the start of your program and drag downward, connecting this beam to your Loop block. To add a tune to your program, drag a sequence of Sound blocks to this loop and set each one to play a different musical note. Both branches of the program will run simultaneously, so that your car will trace a cloverleaf while playing a tune.

Once both branches of your program are complete, you are ready to make adjustments. To do this, you will download just the cloverleaf branch of your program to your car by highlighting just that branch and downloading it using the Download and Run Selected button in the upper right corner. Adjust the steering and timing in your program in order to perfect your cloverleaf. Once you are satisfied with it, download and run the entire program.

Teacher Information   Cloverleaf

The students write their own programs to trace figure-eight patterns. They learn how to add a second sequence beam to a program.

Objectives
1. To write a program containing parallel sequence beams.
2. To gain practice writing multi-step programs.
3. To use the Download and Run Selected button to test part of a program.

Materials
NXT car from the previous activity
Computer

Time: Approximately 40 minutes

Notes
1. If the students do not already have cars, any simple two-motor cars can be used for this activity. See sample designs for simple two-motor cars in the Introductory Activities section.
2. Once the students have written and tested the basic program, have them adjust the power, duration, and degree of turning to produce a cloverleaf.
3. The motion of the cars will vary depending upon the floor surface, battery power, etc.

Sample Program for Cloverleaf

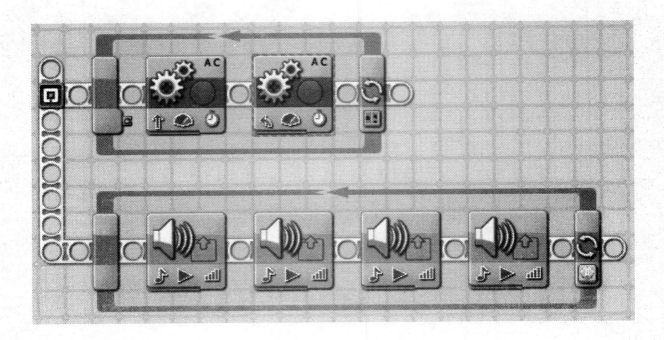

Top Loop block:

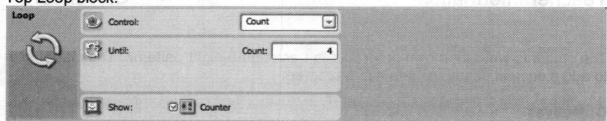

First Move block:

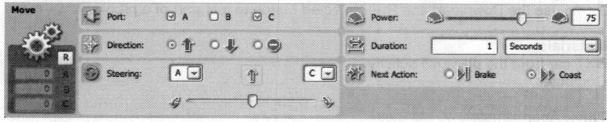

Second Move block:

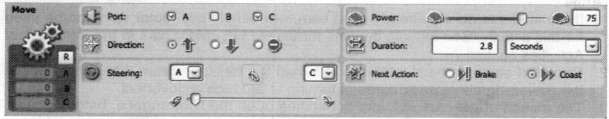

Bottom Loop block:

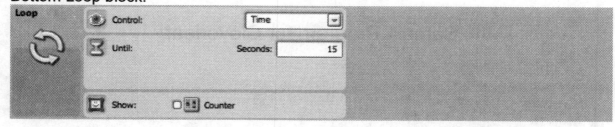

Programming Practice and Quiz

To ensure that every student has mastered the basics of programming using the Common Palette, the teacher can end the unit by administering a brief quiz. The quiz is a straightforward review of the basic concepts; its point is merely to allow the students to demonstrate competence at programming.

The accountability provided by the quiz is particularly important if students have been working in groups. It helps to ensure that every member of the group has learned to program. In fact, announcing the quiz at the beginning of the unit will often spur the students to make sure that they take in active role in programming.

Before giving the quiz, assign the practice sheet to the students to help them identify any gaps in their knowledge.

Answers to Common Palette Programming Practice

1. The program turns on motors A and C going forward at full power when the light sensor on port 3 registers a light level above 60. If the light level is at or below 60, the motors turn off.
2. An eye on the NXT display opens and shuts at one-second intervals.

Answers to Common Palette Programming Quiz

1. While the touch sensor on port 1 is pressed, the musical note A plays. If the touch sensor is not being pressed, no sound is played. The program loops forever.
2. The motors on ports A and C run at full power steering first in one direction for two seconds and then in the other for two seconds. This snake-like motion repeats for a total of five S-shaped sequences. The motors shut off and the program ends.

Common Palette Programming Practice

Explain what the following programs do, step by step. Be sure to note which port each motor or sensor is plugged into.

1.

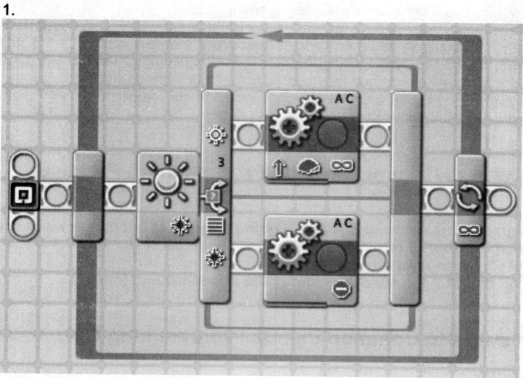

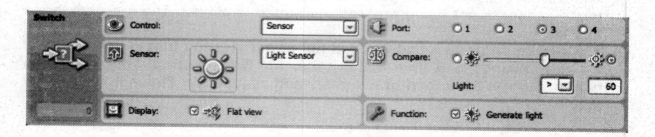

2.

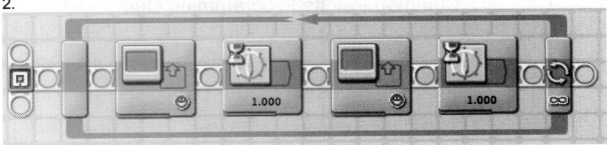

First Display block:

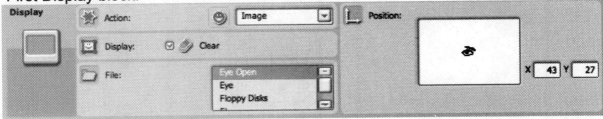

Second Display block:

Common Palette Programming Quiz

Explain what the following programs do, step by step. Be sure to note which port each motor or sensor is plugged into.

1.

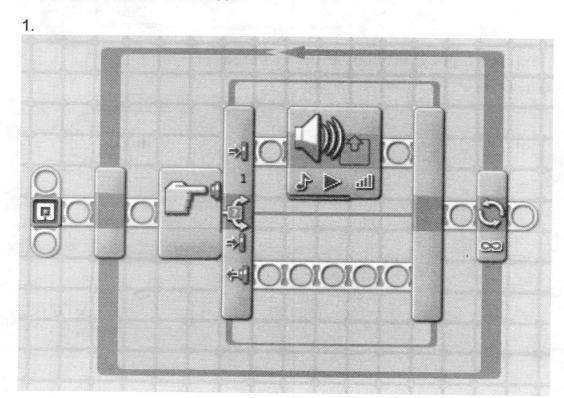

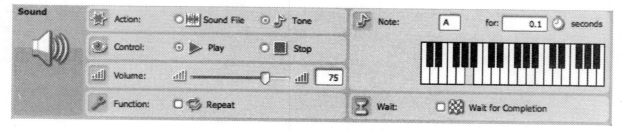

2.

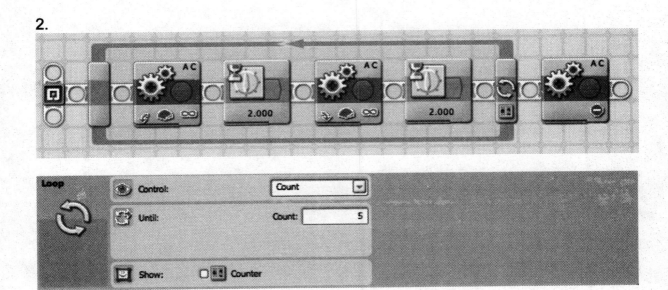

Part Four: Complete Palette Activities

This set of activities introduces the Complete Palette, including working with data hubs.

The activities in this section are:
1. Clap On
2. Daytime Fan
3. Snail Trail
4. Roll of the Die
5. Three-Speed Fan
6. Dog Years

These six activities are designed to be done in order. The students, working in pairs, complete the activities at their own pace. As they finish each one, they have the resulting program approved by the teacher before moving to the next activity.

One way of organizing these activities is to give each student a Complete Understanding sheet to fill out as he or she works. When a student successfully completes an activity, he or she brings the NXT containing the program to the teacher for inspection. The teacher checks that the program fulfills the activity's requirements, and approves it by stamping the student's Complete Understanding sheet in the appropriate box. The student is then free to move on to the next activity.

Using Complete Understanding allows the teacher to keep track of every student's progress while concentrating on helping those who need the most assistance. Because each student hands in a single stamped sheet at the end of the sequence, the grading for the unit can be done very efficiently.

A quiz is included at the end of the chapter to test the students' understanding of Complete Palette programming.

Complete Understanding

When you complete each sheet, demonstrate your program to the teacher. Make sure that you get the stamp of approval for each activity before moving on to the next one.

Clap On	
Daytime Fan	
Snail Trail	
Roll of the Die	
Three-Speed Fan	
Dog Years	

Clap On

The Complete Palette in the NXT Mindstorms software contains all of the blocks of the Common Palette, plus many more. To access the Complete Palette, click on the Complete Palette tab in the lower left corner, the one that shows three blocks on a diagonal.

Notice that the first set of blocks on the Complete Palette is the familiar Common Palette. Most of the blocks in the Common Palette also appear in the appropriate categories of the Complete Palette—Move, Sound, and Display under Action; Wait, Loop, and Switch under Flow.

As you work on this activity, use the blocks in Action and Flow, so that you become accustomed to using the expanded palette. You will also be using one block that does not appear in the Common Palette, the Lamp block, which turns on the lamp brick.

Your task: A device advertised on late-night television allows you to turn your lights on and off by clapping. Build such a device for the NXT. When you clap, the light should turn on. When you clap again, the light should turn off. The program should repeat over and over.

To detect the clap, use the Wait for Sound block . The default value is to wait until the sound level is greater than 50; depending upon the noise level in the room and the loudness of your clap, you may need to adjust the number.

To turn on the light, use the Lamp block , located in the Action section.

After the light turns on or off, you will need to make the device wait for a second before listening for another clap. Otherwise, the device may turn on and off multiple times from a single clap.

Teacher Information

Clap On

This activity introduces the lamp brick and the Complete Palette.

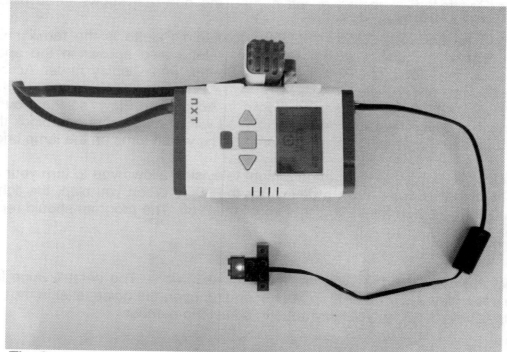

The lamp on this clap-on/clap-off device has a blue semitransparent brick over it.

Objectives
1. To be able to locate and use blocks in the Complete Palette.
2. To learn how to use the lamp brick.

Materials
NXT
Computer
Sound sensor
Lamp brick

Time: Approximately 20 minutes

Notes
1. With the exception of the Lamp block, all of the blocks used in this program can be found in the Common Palette. Even so, encourage the students to find and use the Complete-Palette versions so that they become accustomed to the larger menu of blocks.

Sample Program for Clap On

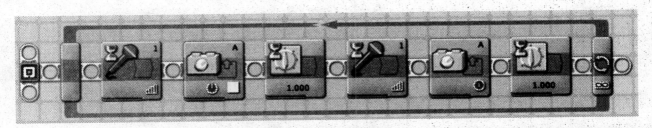

This program waits until it perceives an increase in the sound level (a clap). It then turns on the light and waits for one second. After another clap, the light turns off. The program pauses for one second, and then repeats.

Daytime Fan

The NXT Mindstorms software allows you to use the information from one block of a program to influence another block. For example, the sequence below would change the brightness of the light based upon the temperature: the higher the temperature, the brighter the light. The information is sent from one block to another by way of a data wire, the line connecting the bottoms of the two blocks.

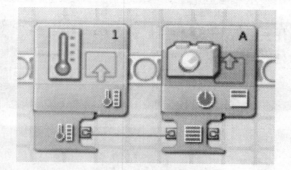

To connect two blocks by a data wire, click on the bottom of a block. An extension of the block will pop out—the data hub. Connect the plug you want to use to the appropriate plug of the other block. In the example, you would connect the Temperature plug on the Temperature Sensor hub to the Intensity plug of the Lamp hub.

Your task: Make a fan that revolves rapidly when the light is bright and slows when the light dims. To power the Motor, use the Motor block, located in the Action section. (Unlike the Move block, which can control multiple motors, the Motor block controls only one motor.) Set the time to Unlimited. Note that to make the motor move fast in the daytime and slowly at night, you will need to check the light level and adjust the motor over and over. How can you accomplish this?

Teacher Information

Daytime Fan

This activity introduces the students to the use of data hubs.

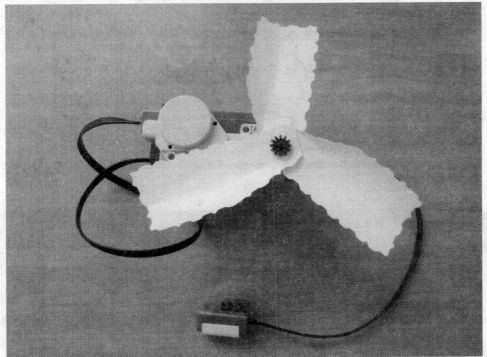

A light-sensor-controlled fan with blades made of thin cardboard.

Objectives
1. To learn how to use data hubs in a program.
2. To be able to wire plugs.
3. To use the Motor block to control a single motor.

Materials
NXT
Computer
Motor
LEGO® pieces
Cardboard for fan blades (optional)

Time: Approximately 30 minutes

Notes
1. At the beginning of this activity, you may want to demonstrate how to use data hubs, plugs, and wires.
2. If the students are working in groups, make sure that each student has an opportunity to practice using data hubs.

Sample Program for Daytime Fan

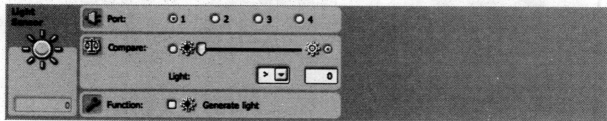

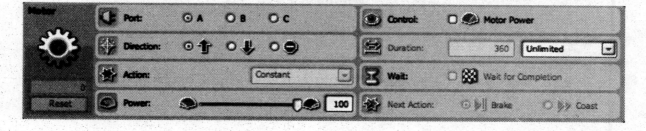

Snail Trail

As you saw earlier, the NXT Mindstorms software allows you to control the small display screen on the NXT. Using the data hubs, you can control the placement—and movement—of images on the screen.

Your task: Make a snail crawl across the screen, starting at the left side of the display and slowing moving to the right. To do this, place a Display block inside a loop and use the loop counter to control the x-coordinate position of the image, by wiring it into the X plug of the Display block.

To make the loop counter plug appear, check the Show Counter box.

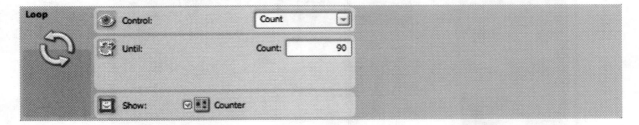

Each time the snail moves, the program should pause for a brief period before shifting the snail's position. If you want a slow snail, use a one-second pause. For a speedier snail, choose a shorter time period.

Teacher Information   Snail Trail

The students learn how to control the NXT display in a program.

A snail crawls across the screen.

Objectives
1. To gain additional practice in using data hubs.
2. To learn how to use the loop counter in a program.
3. To learn how to control the NXT screen in a program

Materials
NXT
Computer

Time
Approximately 20 minutes

Notes
1. You may want to review coordinates before beginning this activity.

Sample Program for Snail Trail

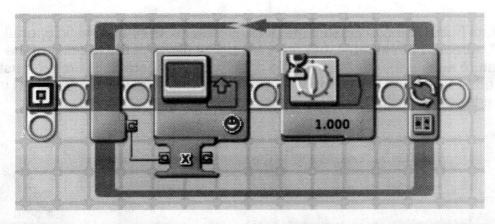

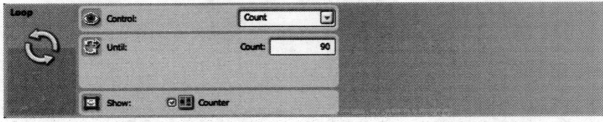

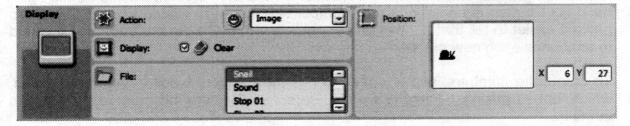

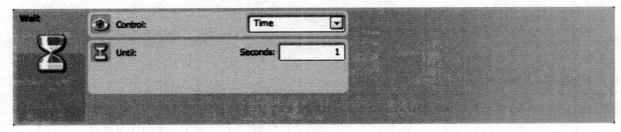

Roll of the Die

Using data hubs, you can display the outputs of sensors or arithmetic operations on the NXT screen. For example, the program below displays the reading of the temperature sensor for one second. To do this, the temperature number must be converted to text using the Number-to-Text block (the one with the 3's on it) in the Advanced section.

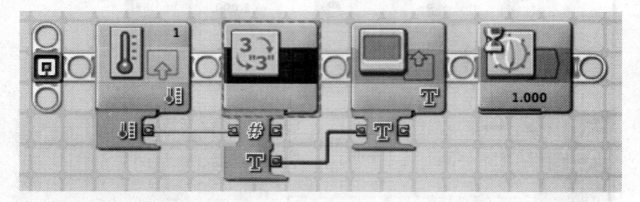

Your task: Write a program that generates a random number between one and six, like throwing a die, and displays the number on the NXT screen. Each time the right-hand NXT button is pressed, a new number should be generated and displayed. To make it easier to tell that a new number has arrived, make the program play a sound to announce each new number.

To create the numbers, you will need to use the Random block in the data section, which, not surprisingly, looks like a die. Be sure to set the minimum and maximum numbers.

Teacher Information

Roll of the Die

The students learn how to use the Number-to-Text and Random blocks.

Objectives
1. To gain additional practice in using data hubs.
2. To learn how to use the Random block.
3. To learn how to use the Number-to-Text block.
4. To learn how to program the NXT buttons.

Materials
NXT
Computer

Time
Approximately 20 minutes

Notes
1. You may want to have the students outline their programs on paper before writing them on the computer. That way, any difficulties they have in structuring the programs can be tackled separately from problems with using data hubs and wiring.
2. Random or Not, in the Mostly Mathematics section, offers a further exploration of the Random block.

Sample Program for Roll of the Die

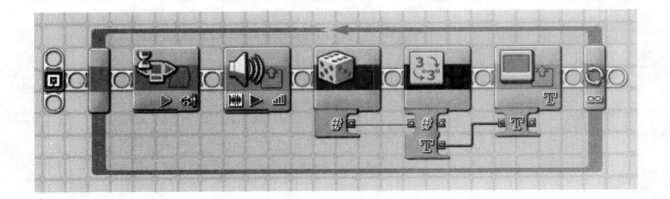

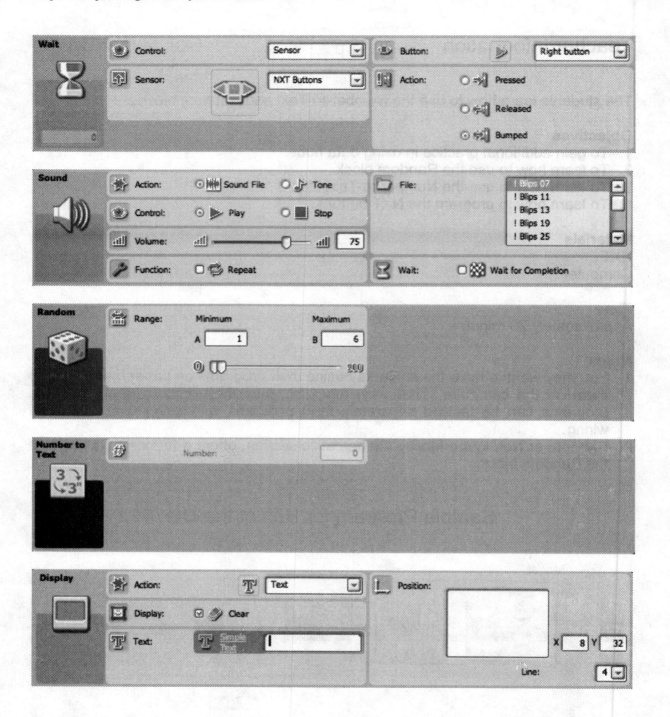

Three-Speed Fan

Sometimes when you are using data hubs, you need to manipulate a value from one block before sending it to another. For example, the following program displays the numbers one through five at one-second intervals. Because the counter is set at zero for the first pass through the loop, the program uses the Math block to add one to the counter before displaying it.

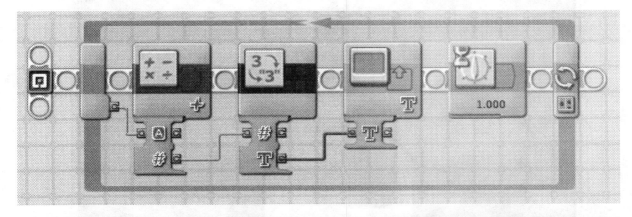

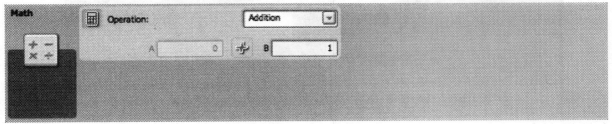

Your task: Make a variable-speed fan. Give your fan four settings: off, low speed, medium speed, and high speed. Use the touch sensor to change the speed.

A few hints: you will need to use nested loops for this program—one loop within another. The outer loop will run forever. The inner loop will run four times. You can use the loop counter for this inner loop to control the motor speed. However, since the motor speed varies between zero and 100, you will need to multiply the loop counter by a constant before using it to run the motor.

Teacher Information   Three-Speed Fan

This activity introduces the Math block and makes use of nested loops.

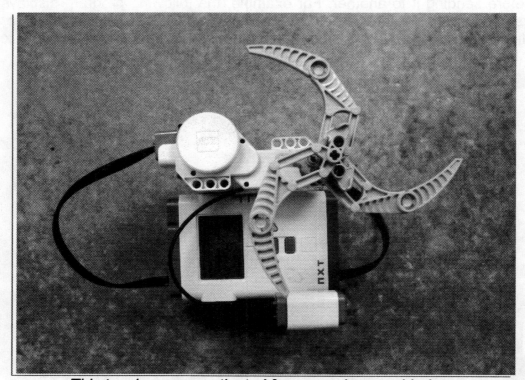

This touch-sensor-activated fan uses claws as blades.

Objectives
1. To be learn how to use the Math block.
2. To use a nested loop.

Materials
NXT
Computer
Motor
Touch sensor
LEGO® pieces
Cardboard for fan blades (optional)

Time: Approximately 30 minutes

Notes
1. You may want to have the students outline their programs on paper before writing them on the computer.
2. You may want to discuss the sample program as a class to make sure that the students understand it before they attempt their own programs.

Sample Program for Three-Speed Fan

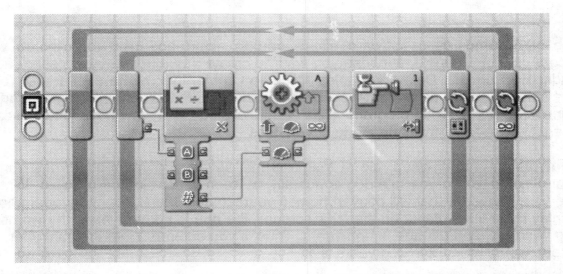

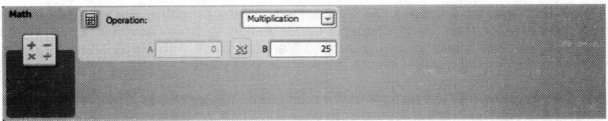

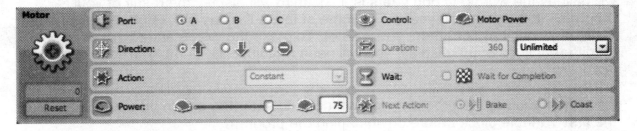

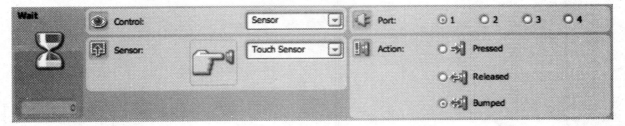

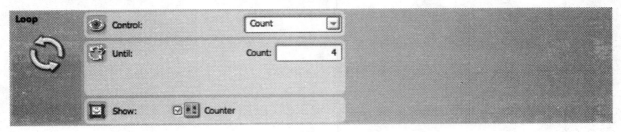

Dog Years

The NXT MIndstorms software allows you to name and use variables in your programs. For example, suppose you want to create a number variable called "age." Under Edit, choose Define Variables. Click on Create, then name the variable "age" and select Number as the dataype. To put your new variable into a program, add a Variable block to your program. (The Variable block is in the advanced section.) Then, choose "age" from the menu of variables.

Your task: An often-used rule of thumb is that seven dog years equal one human year. That is, a two-year-old dog is actually fourteen years old in dog years. Write a dog-year converter that will convert human years to dog years. Your converter should display three lines of text on the NXT screen—the age in human years, the words "in dog years is," and the age in dog years. Thus, if you entered 2 into the converter, the screen would read, "2 in dog years is 14."

Dog Years requires a variable. At the beginning of the program, you will need to use a Variable block with Write checked under Action to enter a value. Later in the program, you will need to use a second Variable block with Read checked under Action to display the number and to convert it to dog years.

For this program, you will also need three different Display blocks. The first one will display the starting number for the converter—the age in human years. The second will display the words "in dog years is." The third will display the result of your program—the age in dog years. For some of these Display blocks, you will want the Clear box checked, for others you will not. To make the words and numbers appear on different lines of the display, you will need to adjust line number in each Display box.

Each time you run the program, you will need to enter the age in human years into the first Variable block before downloading the program.

Teacher Information   Dog Years

This activity introduces the use of variables and gives additional practice in using the Math and Display blocks.

Objectives
1. To be learn how to use variables.
2. To use multiple Display blocks to modify a single NXT screen.
3. To gain additional practice in using the Math block and data hubs.

Materials
NXT
Computer

Time: Approximately 30 minutes

Notes
1. You may want to have the students outline their programs on paper before writing them on the computer.
2. You may want to demonstrate how to create and name variables before beginning this activity.

Sample Program for Dog Years

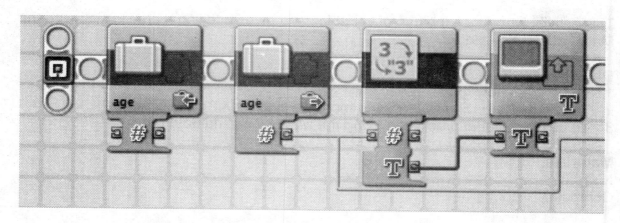

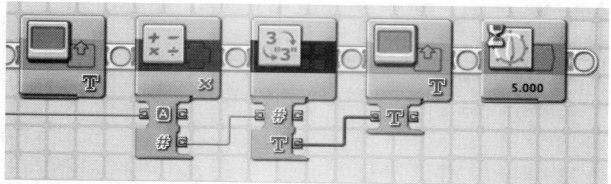

First Variable block:

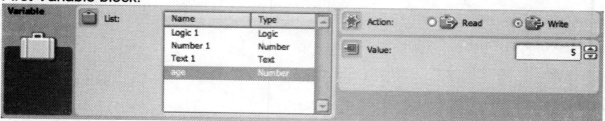

Second Variable block:

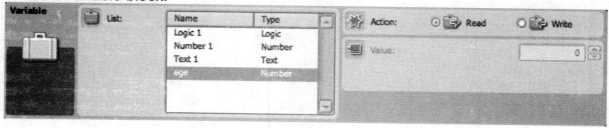

First Display block:

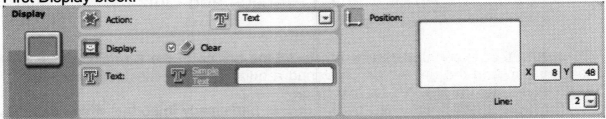

Second Display block:

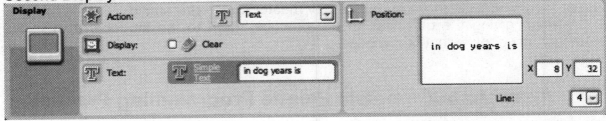

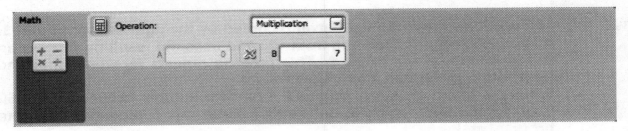

Third Display block:

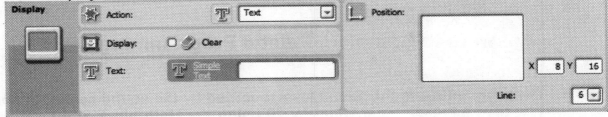

Programming Practice and Quiz

To ensure that every student has mastered the basics of the Complete Palette, the teacher can end the unit by administering a quiz. The quiz includes data hubs, the Math block, and the Number-to-Text block.

The accountability provided by the quiz is particularly important if students have been working in groups. It helps to ensure that every member of the group has learned to program. In fact, announcing the quiz at the beginning of the unit will often spur the students to make sure that they master the programming.

Before giving the quiz, assign the practice sheet to the students to help them identify any gaps in their knowledge.

Answers to Complete Palette Programming Practice

1. **The program reads the light level recorded by the light sensor in port 3. It then subtracts that reading from 100 and uses the resulting number as the motor power for motor A. This process repeats forever. So, as the light gets brighter, the motor slows down.**
2. **When the touch sensor is bumped, a random number between 0 and 60 is generated and displayed on the NXT screen for 5 seconds. Then, the program ends.**

Answers to Complete Palette Programming Quiz

1. **The program reads the sound level recorded by the sound sensor in port 1. It then increases that value by 20 using the Math block and uses the resulting number as the motor power for motors A and C. This process repeats forever.**
2. **The program displays the words "Light level =" on the NXT screen, followed by the light level reading recorded by the light sensor in port 3. The words remain on the screen until the touch sensor is pressed, ending the program.**

Complete Palette Programming Practice

What does each of the following programs do?

1.

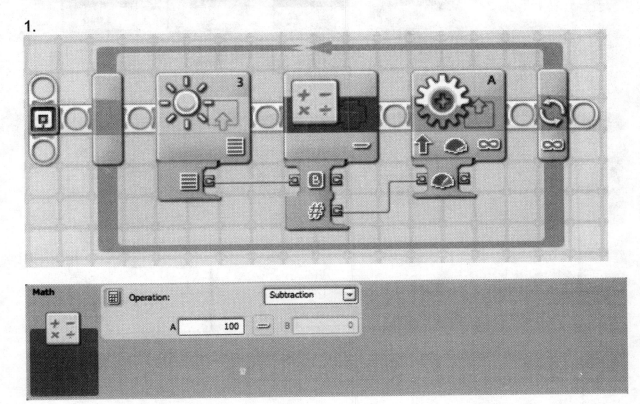

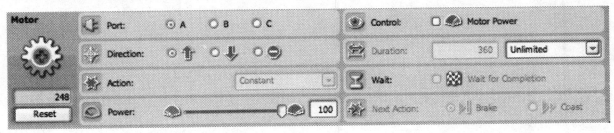

2.

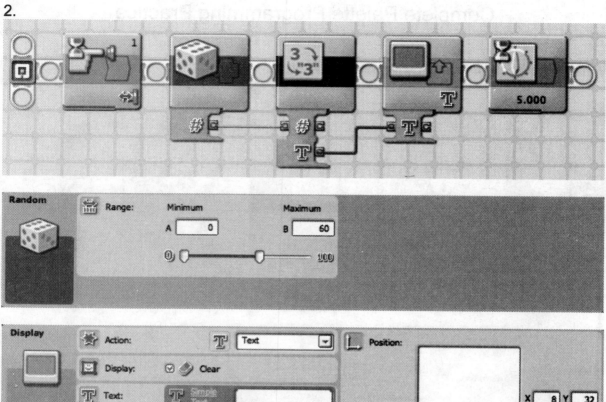

Complete Palette Programming Quiz

Explain what each of the following programs does.

1.

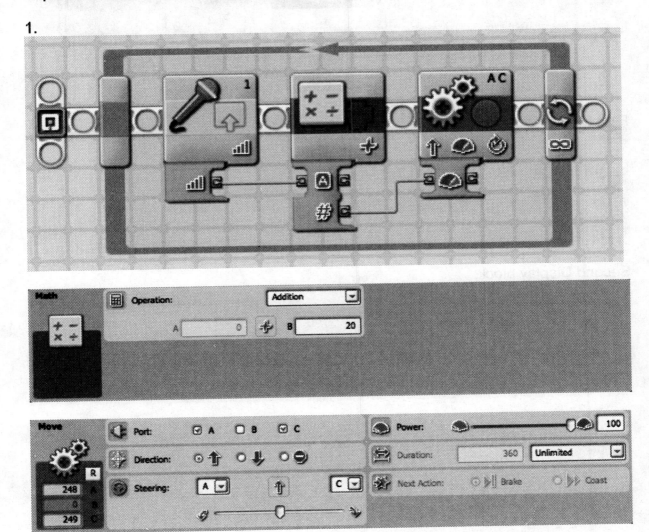

2.

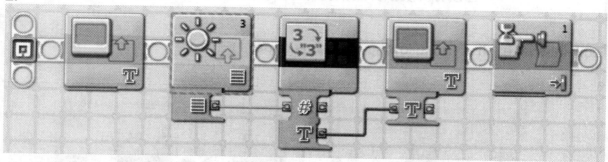

First Display block:

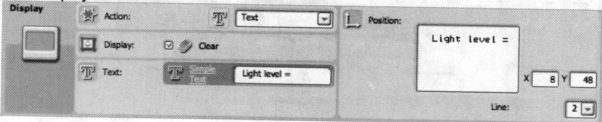

Second Display block:

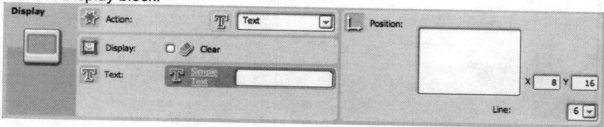

Part Five: Projects

These projects use the building and programming skills that the students have mastered. Some projects involve solving a challenge (Haunted House, Bug in a Box), while others emphasize the creative use of building and programming (Music Box, Meet and Greet). The last five projects are more complicated and could be used as culminating activities.

The activities in this section are:
1. Music Box
2. Haunted House
3. Meet and Greet
4. Bug in a Box
5. Outside the Box
6. Clean Sweep
7. Applause Meter
8. Mini Golf
9. Robotic Zoo
10. Chain Reaction Machine
11. EGGcellent Contraption
12. Wacky Gumball Machine

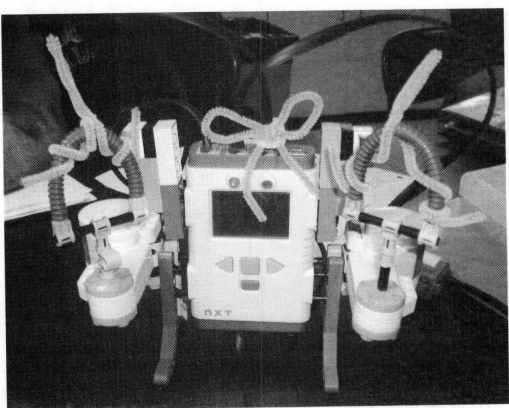

Pipe cleaners and other craft materials help to enliven projects.

Music Box

Build a music box in which figures move while music plays. Your box must have a theme with appropriate music, figures, and decorations.

Your music box must include two or more figures that move in different ways. At least one must move back and forth or up and down.

Have fun!

1. Title of your music box:

2. Theme of your music box:

3. Music played:

4. Describe your figures/action/storyline:

5. Sketch and describe the mechanism you used to create back-and-forth movement:

Creating Back-and-Forth Motion with the NXT Motor

Using a cam to create up-and down motion.

Using a gear rack to create back-and-forth motion.

For other methods of creating back-and-forth motion, see the Examples of Legs page in the activity No Wheels.

Teacher Information   Music Box

The students build music boxes with themes of their choice.

This music box includes different types of motion. The motor in the foreground is being used with a gear rack to create back-and-forth movement. The rear motor is being used with spur gears to make the three couples in the back spin.

Objectives
1. To write a NXT Mindstorms program that plays music.
2. To create figures that move in different ways, including back-and-forth or up-and-down movement.

Materials
NXT
Computer
Motors
LEGO® pieces, including minifigures and decorative elements.

Time: Approximately 90 minutes

Notes
1. There are two options for adding music to an NXT Mindstorms project. The first, rather laborious, method is to add the notes one by one using Sound blocks. The resulting song can be saved as a custom block. The second, and much easier, method is to download songs from LEGOengineering.com. To do this, go to the

LEGOengineering website, choose Resources and Downloads, then Library, then Music, then NXT Software. Select the song you wish to download and follow the accompanying instructions.

2. The volume on the NXT can be adjusted. To do so, starting at the My Files screen, press the right arrow button repeatedly until you reach Settings. Push the orange button; the screen should now say Volume. Press the orange button again and then use the right and left arrow buttons to adjust the volume. Press the orange button to select your choice and return to the Settings screen.

3. This project can be fairly simple or impressively elaborate, depending upon the time available.

4. Many of the students enjoy the creative license that this project affords them. If possible, arrange a way for the students to share their creations with an audience, perhaps a class of younger students.

5. You may want to provide some examples of ways to create back-and-forth movement, to help the students get started. The Creating Back-and-Forth Motion page shows two possibilities; two others are shown on the Examples of Legs page of the activity No Wheels.

This music box uses DUPLO animals.

Haunted House

Your vehicle must find its way through a haunted house. The house has four rooms; your goal is to visit all four. For each room you reach, you will receive a prize.

The rooms will consist of white rectangles on a black background. The rooms will be numbered one through four; you must visit them in order. Once you have visited all four rooms, you may leave through the front door to collect an additional prize.

If you drive completely off the black paper or visit a room out of order, your turn is over.

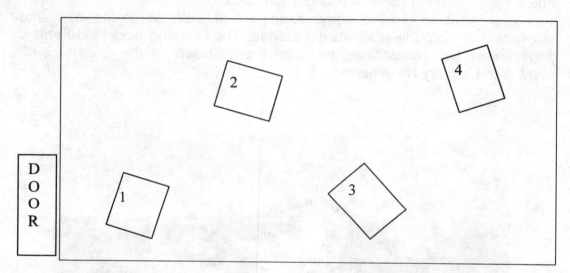

Good luck!

Teacher Information   Haunted House

The students build vehicles and program them to drive through the rooms of a haunted house.

A student watches as his car navigates the haunted house using the motors' built-in rotation sensors.

Objectives
1. To build a sturdy NXT car that turns easily.
2. To program a car to follow a specified route, using rotation sensors, a light sensor, timers, or some combination of these.
3. To solve an open-ended problem.
4. To test and modify a design repeatedly.

Materials
NXT
Computer
Motors
Light sensor (optional)
LEGO® pieces, including wheels
Large sheet of black paper, approximately 90 cm by 120 cm
Four sheets of white paper, approximately 20 cm by 30 cm
Prizes

Time: Approximately 80 minutes

Notes

1. To construct the haunted house, start with a large sheet of black paper, approximately 90 cm by 120 cm. (If necessary, you can glue smaller sheets together.) Glue or tape four white sheets on the black field, as shown on the student handout, making sure the edges are securely fastened. Number each room. If you prefer, you can instead use a white house with black rooms

2. Any simple two-motor car that turns easily will work for this activity. If the students need help in designing a car that turns easily, you may want to suggest that they use a caster wheel or a slider in the front instead of a fixed wheel or wheels.

3. This activity is well suited to the NXT's built-in rotation sensors. The sensors can be used to drive the distance between rooms consistently and precisely.

4. Another possible strategy is to use a light sensor mounted on the car to determine when the car has reached a room. A timer can be used to accomplish the turns within rooms.

5. Another method that can be used to guide the car is a dead-reckoning program, where the car is programmed to drive for a specified number of seconds, and then turn for some number of seconds, then drive, and so on. This strategy is initially easier than using a sensor, but gives less consistent results (especially if the battery power declines as the car is tested repeatedly).

6. Let the students try their cars in the haunted house as often as they wish. The process of testing and reprogramming is an essential part of this activity.

7. Have token prizes available for successfully completing each room. (If you do this activity near Halloween, many inexpensive Halloween-themed trinkets are available from novelty companies.) One way of handling the prizes is to award each group a numbered card for each room they visit. At the end of the activity, the cards can be redeemed for prizes.

Sample Program for Haunted House

First Move block:

Second Move block:

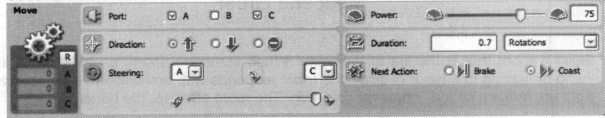

Third Move block:

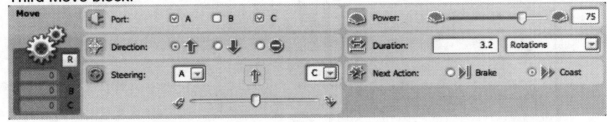

Fourth Move block:

Fifth Move block:

This program uses the built-in rotation sensors to guide the car through the first three rooms of the haunted house.

Acknowledgement

This activity is adapted from a similar one by Merredith Portsmore, Center for Engineering Education and Outreach, Tufts University.

Meet and Greet

Build a robot that is the life of the party. When someone greets it—by shaking its hand or waving to it (your choice), the robot responds with enthusiasm. It can move, light up, make a sound, whatever you wish. The more effusive, the better.

1. What does your robot look like? Draw a sketch and write a brief description.

2. How is the robot activated? Describe the mechanism you used.

3. What does the robot do when you greet it?

Teacher Information   Meet and Greet

The students build robotic pals who greet newcomers with enthusiasm.

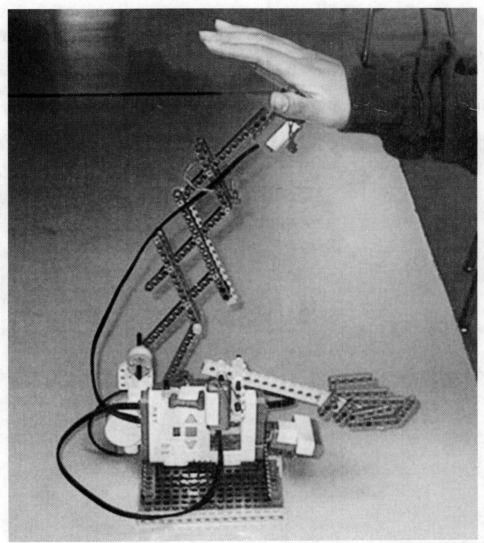

This "high-five" bot gives you a high five after you shake its hand.

Objectives
1. To write a program in which a sensor initiates the action.
2. To find a creative solution to a challenge.

Materials
NXT
Computer
Motor(s)
Light sensor or touch sensor

LEGO® pieces, including decorative elements
Craft materials

Time: Approximately 60 minutes

Notes
1. This project can be simple or elaborate, depending upon the time available. Many of the students enjoy the creative license that this project affords them.
2. If the students choose to have the pal activated by a handshake, they can use a touch sensor. For a wave-activated pal, a light sensor can be used instead.
3. The features of the pal can be done with LEGO pieces, craft materials, or both.

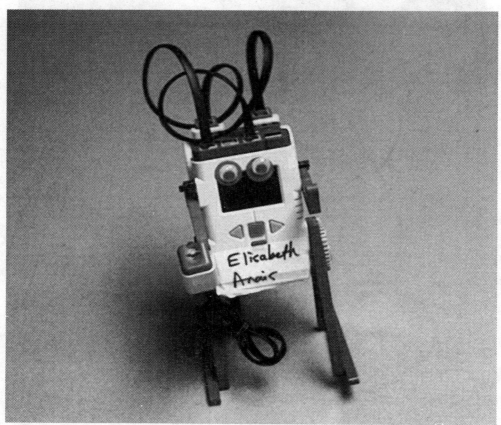

This dancing Meet and Greet robot picks up its feet one at a time.

Bug in a Box

Build a bug and program it to scuttle around in a box.

Here are the guidelines:

First, your bug must be constantly moving. If it spins in place, it cannot stay in that one spot for more than five seconds.

Second, it must stay in the box for at least thirty seconds. The "box" will be a large sheet of white paper with sides consisting of thick black lines. Your bug may stick part of its body over a line, but if it leaves the box completely it is disqualified.

Good luck!

1. How did you build your bug? Describe how you made the bug able to turn and maneuver easily.

2. How did you keep the bug in the box? Describe your program and how it dealt with the bug reaching a line.

Teacher Information

Bug in a Box

The students build bugs that can stay in a box for thirty seconds

An elaborate NXT bug navigates the box. One motor of the bug controls the rack-and-pinion steering mechanism; the second powers both back wheels.

Objectives
1. To write a program that uses a light sensor.
2. To create a vehicle that turns easily.
3. To solve an open-ended problem.
4. To test and modify a design repeatedly.

Materials
NXT
Computer
Motors
Light sensor
LEGO® pieces, including wheels
White paper and black tape to make the box

Time: Approximately 40 minutes

Notes

1. This challenge is somewhat less forgiving than the following one, Outside the Box. In Bug in a Box, thirty seconds is generally enough time to expose any flaws in the algorithms that the students are using. In Outside the Box, a wider variety of programs will be successful.
2. To build the box, make a large square or rectangle with thick black tape on a white background. The smaller the shape, the harder the challenge. One-meter-long sides make a satisfying but not–too-difficult box. To make the challenge easier, you can use a circular boundary instead of a square one.
3. Let the students try their bug in the box as often as they wish. The process of testing and redesigning is an essential part of this activity.
4. The light sensor works best if it is placed close to the ground and facing the floor.

Sample Program for Bug in a Box

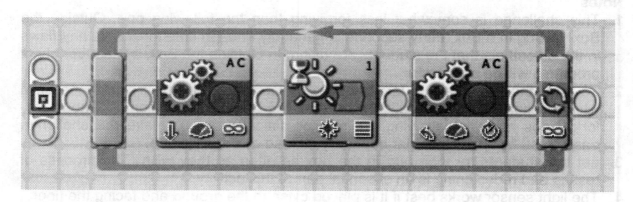

First Move block:

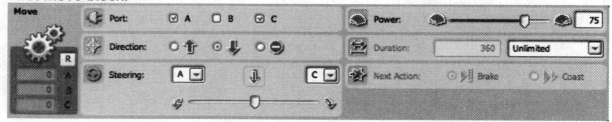

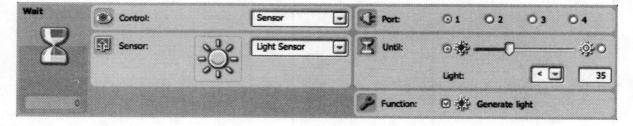

Second Move block:

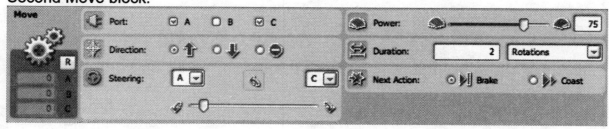

Outside the Box

Build a bug and program it to escape from a box.

The "box" will be a large sheet of white paper with sides consisting of thick black lines. Your bug must find the gap in the black line and escape through it. Your bug may stick part of its body over a line, but if it leaves the box completely by crossing the black line, it is disqualified.

Good luck!

1. How did you build your bug? Describe how you made the bug able to turn and maneuver easily.

2. How did you program your bug to explore all sides of the box looking for the gap? Describe your program and how it dealt with the bug reaching a line.

Teacher Information

Outside the Box

The students build bugs that escape from a box as quickly as possible.

Objectives
1. To write a program that uses a light sensor.
2. To create a vehicle that turns easily.
3. To solve an open-ended problem.
4. To test and modify a design repeatedly.

Materials
NXT
Computer
Motors
Light sensor
LEGO® pieces, including wheels
White paper and black tape to make the box

Time: Approximately 30 minutes

Notes
1. This challenge is somewhat more forgiving than the previous one, Bug in a Box. A wider variety of programs will be successful here. In Bug in a Box, thirty seconds is generally enough time to expose any flaws in the algorithms that the students are using.
2. To build the box, make a large square or rectangle with thick black tape on a white background. Leave a thirty-centimeter gap in the tape on one side to create the opening. Of course, you can adjust the size of the opening to make the activity harder or easier.
3. Let the students try their bug in the box as often as they wish. The process of testing and redesigning is an essential part of this activity.
4. The light sensor works best if it is placed close to the ground and facing the floor.

Sample Program for Outside the Box

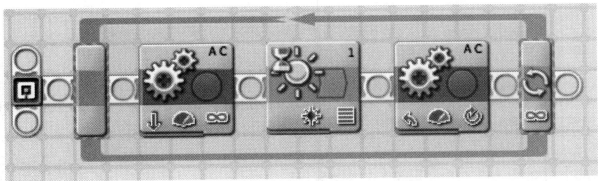

First Move block:

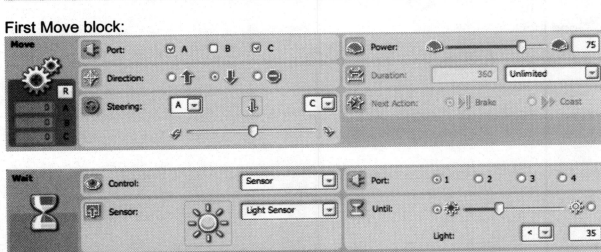

Second Move block:

Clean Sweep

The task: Build and program a sweeping machine to clear a large area quickly. The vehicle should have two motors, each controlled by a touch sensor attached to a cable.

The challenge: You will have thirty seconds to clear a large square containing LEGO® bricks. You will earn a point for each brick you are able to push completely out of the square in that time.

The catch: Your sweeper must be small enough to fit in a closet for storage. It can be no longer or wider than 30 centimeters.

Good luck!

Teacher Information   Clean Sweep

This activity makes use of the programming skills that the students have learned.

Obstacles may be placed around the clean sweep field to make the challenge more difficult.

Objectives
1. To write a program containing multiple loops and switches.
2. To construct a plow or other device for moving objects.

Materials
NXT
Computer
Motors
Touch sensors
LEGO® pieces, including wheels and bricks
Tape for making the boundaries of the playing field
Obstacles (optional)

Time: Approximately 50 minutes

Notes

1. This activity follows naturally from the programming activities in Common Sense, which makes it a good culminating activity for the Common-Sense programming sequence. Each touch sensor runs one of the motors; by pushing one or both of the touch sensors, the driver can make the car turn or go straight.

2. A reasonable playing field is a square one meter on each side, containing 100 2 x 2 or 2 x 4 LEGO® bricks.

3. Most groups will attach some sort of plow to the front of the sweeper to push bricks out of the way. If you wish, you can remove the size restriction and let the students try very long plows.

4. You may wish to award prizes for successfully removing bricks from the field, perhaps a small reward for every ten bricks removed, plus a larger reward for a clean sweep.

Sample Program for Clean Sweep

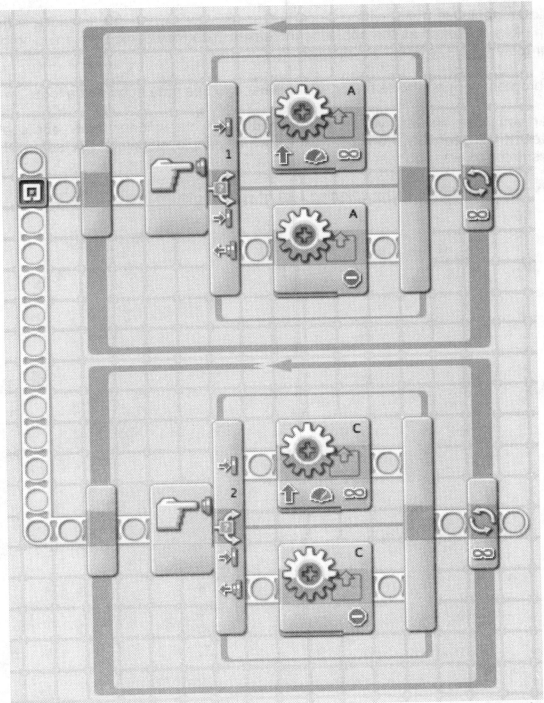

Pressing the touch sensor connected to port 1 turns on motor A. Pressing the touch sensor connected to port 3 turns on motor C. Releasing a touch sensor turns off the corresponding motor.

Applause Meter

Build an applause meter with a piece that spins slowly when the applause is muted, then picks up speed as the applause increases. You may design the spinning part of your meter to be as fancy as you wish.

To program your applause meter, you will need to use data hubs and a loop.

After you have finished your program and built your spinner, test your applause meter. It will probably work best with several people clapping; ask some of your classmates to help you test it.

1. Make a sketch of the spinning part of your applause meter.

Teacher Information

Applause Meter

In this activity, the students construct applause meters that use the noise level to control the motor speed.

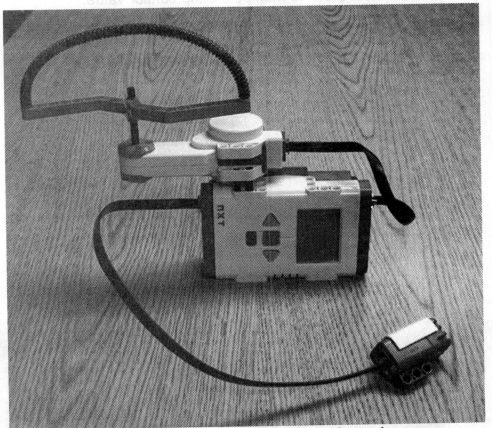

This applause meter spins faster as the applause increases.

Objectives
1. To use the sound level to control the motor power.
2. To gain experience using sensors and data hubs.

Materials
NXT
Computer
Sound sensor
Motor
LEGO® parts

Time: Approximately 40 minutes

Notes
1. The students should be comfortable using data hubs before doing this activity.
2. The activity Musical Instrument is a good choice to follow this one. The program is similar, but adds a Math block to manipulate the sensor value.

Sample Program for Applause Meter

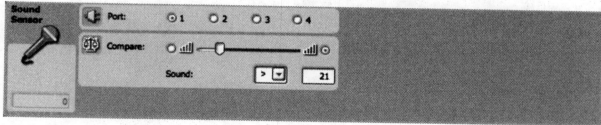

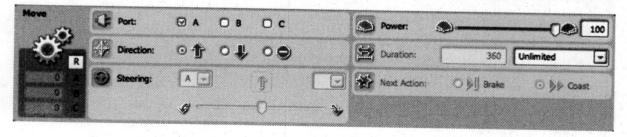

Answer to Applause Meter

1. **Answers will vary.**

Mini Golf

As a class, we will build a miniature golf course. The "golf ball" for our course will be a marble. Each group will be responsible for designing and constructing one hole. You may use LEGO® pieces and any other materials you wish.

Here are the rules:

1. Your hole must include a starting tee of some type and an ending spot. The ball, if hit correctly from the starting tee, should traverse the path through your hole and finish at the ending spot.
2. Your hole must use an NXT and at least one sensor. Some action (movement, sound, lights, etc.) must happen in response to the ball.
3. Your design must have a theme, such as pirates or penguins. Once you have decided on a theme, register it with the teacher. Themes are first come, first served—if some other group has already registered the brilliant idea that you planned to use, you will have to think of another theme.

Documentation:

1. After each work session, you must write a daily log. It should be detailed, complete, and thoughtful. Sketches are always helpful. If you are absent, you still need to fill out a sheet, noting that you were absent and describing what your group did that day.
2. Once your hole is finished, write a detailed description of it and make labeled sketches of the mechanisms involved.

Good luck!

Mini Golf Daily Log

1. Date:

2. Today I worked on:

3. One success I had today was:

4. One difficulty I had today was:

5. Tomorrow I plan to:

Teacher Information   Mini Golf

The class designs a mini-golf course, with each group designing and constructing one hole.

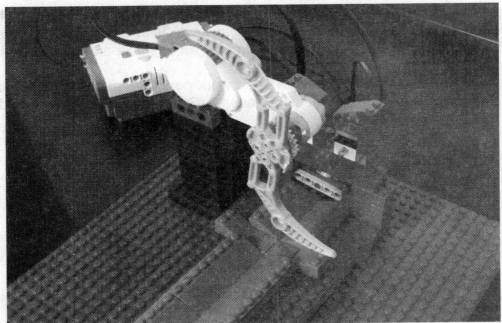

At the end of this hole on the golf course, the ball must pass by the rotating claws to reach the monster's mouth. Once it does, a touch sensor in the mouth causes the monster's eyes to light up.

Objectives
1. To write a complex program that includes sensors.
2. To design and build a complicated mechanical structure.
3. To plan and carry out a major design project.

Materials
Marbles or metal ball bearings
NXT
Computer
Motors
Sensors
LEGO® pieces, including decorative elements
Craft materials (optional)

Time: Approximately 120 minutes

Notes

1. This project can be fairly simple or impressively elaborate, depending upon the time available.
2. Many of the students enjoy the creative license that this project affords them. If possible, arrange a way for the students to share their creations with an audience, perhaps a class of younger students.
3. The decorations can be done using LEGO® pieces, craft materials, or both.
4. This project can also be done on a larger scale with standard golf balls. If golf balls are used, have the students design only an obstacle around the ending spot, rather than the entire hole from tee to end.
5. Assigning a daily log at the end of each work period helps the students organize their time and document the design process. (See the sample log included.)

Robotic Zoo

Build an animal for the robotic zoo. It can be a land animal, a sea creature, an insect, a bird—it does not have to be an animal that is traditionally found in a zoo.

Here are the guidelines:
1. The animal must move in some way. The movement can be walking, or it can be opening and closing jaws, wagging a tail--whatever makes sense for your animal. If your animal does several types of movement, all the better.
2. The animal must use at least one sensor and react to a change in its environment.
3. Accessories are encouraged. Try building your animal a tree to swing in, a den to hide in, or prey to catch.
4. You may add non-LEGO® materials to your animal.

Documentation:
1. After each work session, you must write a daily log. It should be detailed, complete, and thoughtful. Sketches are always helpful. If you are absent, you still need to fill out a sheet, noting that you were absent and describing what your group did that day.
2. Once your animal is finished, write a detailed description of it and make labeled sketches of the mechanisms involved. Take a photograph of your animal.

Good luck!

Robotic Zoo Daily Log

1. Date:

2. Today I worked on:

3. One success I had today was:

4. One difficulty I had today was:

5. Tomorrow I plan to:

Teacher Information

Robotic Zoo

The students design and construct robotic animals.

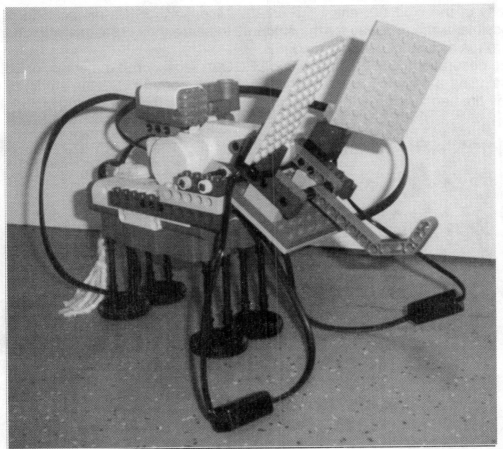

A robotic elephant. It responds to movement by flapping its ears and to sound by nodding its head.

Objectives
1. To write a complex program that includes sensors.
2. To design and build a complicated mechanical structure.
3. To plan and carry out a major design project.

Materials
NXT
Computer
Motors
Sensors
LEGO® pieces, including decorative elements
Craft materials

Time: Approximately 150 minutes

Notes
1. This project can be fairly simple or impressively elaborate, depending upon the time available.
2. Many of the students enjoy the creative license that this project affords them. If possible, arrange a way for the students to share their creations with an audience, perhaps a class of younger students.
3. The decorations can be done using LEGO® pieces, craft materials, or both.
4. Assigning a daily log at the end of each work period helps the students organize their time and document the design process. (See the sample log included.)

A sensor-activated eagle sweeps across a stairwell.

Chain Reaction Machine

We will build a class contraption that carries a marble from one end to the other. Each group will design and build one section.

Here are the minimum requirements for your section:

1. Its footprint can be no larger than 60 cm long or wide (but it can be as high as you want).
2. Your contraption must accept the marble at a height of 10 cm and deliver it to the next contraption at the same height. The marble must be moving at a reasonable pace when it leaves your contraption.
3. The marble must have a height change of at least ten centimeters in the contraption. Since the marble must enter or leave at the same height, it will need to go up and back down—or down and back up.
4. The marble must take at least 15 seconds to traverse your section (longer is better!).
5. Your section must contain at least one sensor and at least one simple machine.

Contraption Checklist

10 centimeters in	
10 centimeters out	
10 centimeter height change	
Simple machine used	
Sensor used	
Marble takes 15 seconds	
Marble traverses machine unaided	

Teacher Information   Chain Reaction Machine

The class designs a chain reaction machine, with each group designing and constructing one section.

Objectives
1. To write a complex program that includes sensors.
2. To design and build a complicated mechanical structure.
3. To plan and carry out a major design project.

Materials
Marbles or metal ball bearings
NXT
Computer
Motors
Sensors
LEGO® pieces
Sheets of cardboard (optional)

Time: Approximately 180 minutes

Notes
1. Large LEGO baseplates or pieces of cardboard make good foundations for the contraptions.
2. This project can be fairly simple or impressively elaborate, depending upon the time available.
3. Many of the students enjoy the creative license that this project affords them. If possible, arrange a way for the students to share their creations with an audience, perhaps a class of younger students.

EGGcellent Contraption

Build an egg-delivery contraption, which will deliver an egg safely from a nest on the table to a collecting plate on the floor.

The nest must contain a sensor that detects when an egg is laid the nest and starts the contraption. The contraption removes the egg from the nest and delivers it to a plate on the floor below, without damaging the egg in any way. The contraption then resets itself, ready for another egg. The contraption must contain two simple machines. When not in use, the contraption must fit in your bin.

Your contraption may be made of LEGO® pieces and/or other materials.

You may test your contraption as often as you wish using plastic eggs weighted with clay. When your contraption can consistently collect plastic eggs, you may try real eggs. Good luck!

Requirement	Possible points	Your points
Started by sensor	10	
Egg removed from nest	10	
Egg removed from nest without damage	5	
Egg transferred from table to floor	10	
Egg transferred to floor without damage	5	
Contraption contains a simple machine	10	
Contains a second simple machine	10	
Contraption resets after egg delivery	10	
Delivers two eggs in a row without damage	5	
Contraption is creative/stylish	5	
Nest looks like a nest	10	
Contraption fits in storage container	10	
Total	**100**	

Teacher Information   EGGcellent Contraption

The students design and construct contraptions to move eggs safely from the table to the floor.

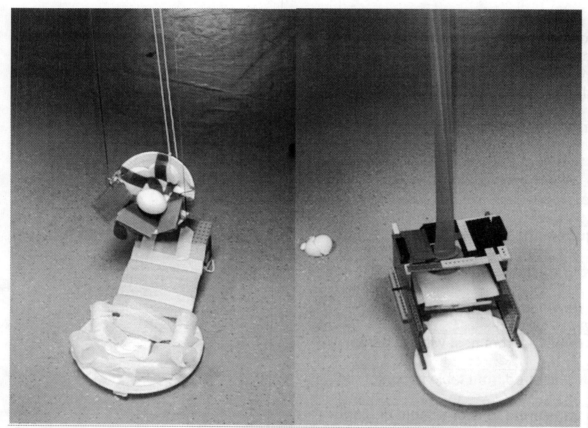

Two methods for lowering the egg to the plate. Left: A plate that tips the egg onto a ramp. Right: A tube made of pantyhose.

Objectives
1. To write a multi-step program that includes sensors.
2. To design and build a complicated mechanical structure.
3. To plan and carry out a major design project.

Materials
NXT
Computer
Motors
Sensors
LEGO® pieces
Plastic eggs
Clay for adding to plastic eggs
Raw eggs
Cleaning supplies (in case of broken eggs)

Plates
String
Other materials for building contraptions

Time: Approximately 180 minutes

Notes
1. Allow plenty of time for testing and modifying the contraptions.
2. The contraptions can be built using LEGO® pieces, craft materials, or both.
3. Many of the students enjoy the creative license that this project affords them. If possible, arrange a way for the students to share their creations with an audience, perhaps a class of younger students.

Wacky Gumball Machine

Build a coin-operated gumball machine. When you place a penny in the slot, the machine delivers a gumball to you. However, the gumball does not just plop out of the machine. Instead, it provides entertainment along the way: for example, activating music, going down a series of chutes, turning a pinwheel—the wackier the better.

We will use marbles to represent the gumballs. For your machine, you may use an NXT, one or more sensors, and LEGO® and non-LEGO building materials. If you need something, just ask!

This project is worth 100 points. The points will be awarded as shown in the chart below. Notice that you can earn as many as twenty extra-credit points by successfully completing everything on the list.

Attribute	Possible points	Your points
Delivers gumball when activated	20	
Includes additional motion started by gumball	20	
Uses sensor	10	
Includes one simple machine	10	
Includes a second simple machine	10	
Activated by coin	10	
Makes music/sounds	10	
Works multiple times without being reset	10	
Delivers exactly one gumball whenever activated	10	

Teacher Information
Wacky Gumball Machine

The students design coin-activated gumball machines.

This machine tosses gumballs at the user one at a time. The user tries to catch the gumballs in a LEGO® box, which is moved by pressing touch sensors.

Objectives
1. To write a complex computer program that includes sensors.
2. To design and build a complicated mechanical structure.
3. To plan and carry out a major design project.

Materials
Marbles or metal ball bearings
NXT
Computer
Motors
Sensors
LEGO pieces

Time: Approximately 180 minutes

Notes

1. This project can be fairly simple or impressively elaborate, depending upon the time available.
2. Many of the students enjoy the creative license that this project affords them. If possible, arrange a way for the students to share their creations with an audience, perhaps a class of younger students.

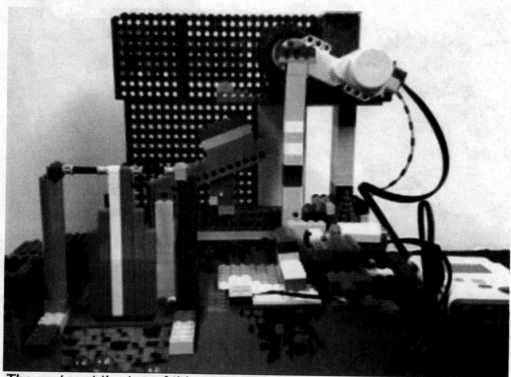

The motor at the top of this gumball machine turns on for a fraction of a second, causing the tire to push a gumball onto the ramp.

Introduction to Data Logging

These labs introduce the students to the data-logging capability of NXT Mindstorms. In addition to learning how to use the software to collect data, the students gain experience in planning and organizing data collection, in working together, and in analyzing the data they have collected.

The activities in this section are:
1. Light and Dark Scavenger Hunt
2. I'm Thinking of a Number
3. Thunderstorm
4. Melting
5. Cave Explorer

The first activity, Light and Dark Scavenger Hunt, serves as an introduction to data logging. It gives the students practice in gathering and uploading data while allowing them to use their creativity to solve a challenge. I'm Thinking of a Number teaches the students how to collect and display multiple data runs, using color to differentiate them. In addition, they gain experience in coordinating the collection of many sets of data and in working as a group. Thunderstorm requires the students to log two sensors simultaneously. They must then interpret a graph containing both sensor outputs. Melting introduces the students to the Prediction tool in NXT Mindstorms. They predict what the temperature curve will look like as ice melts, then perform the experiment to compare the actual data with their predictions. Cave Explorer incorporates data logging into a larger program that runs motors. The activity also combines multiple sensors and multiple data sets. After collecting the data, the students must analyze them by comparing the experimental data to data from a control.

Light and Dark Scavenger Hunt

Your challenge is to find the highest and lowest light readings you can and to record them using the data-logging program.

Open the Mindstorms NXT Data-Logging software. Start a new data-logging program by highlighting "Experiment-1" under Start New Experiment.

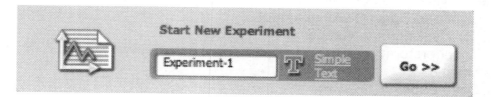

Type in "Scavenger Hunt." Then click on Go. A new data-logging program will open.

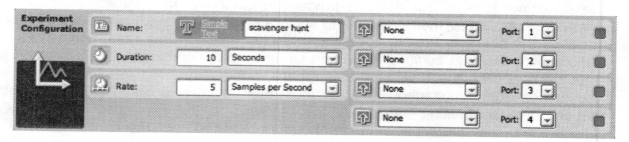

Adjust the program to record light-sensor data on port 1 five times per second for thirty seconds. Turn off the generated light on the light sensor by unchecking the box in the upper right corner.

Connect your NXT to the computer using the USB cable. Attach a light sensor to port 1. Download your program to the NXT using the Download and Run button. As soon as the program is downloaded, the NXT will begin collecting light-sensor data and sending it to the computer. Try moving around the light sensor without disconnecting the USB cable. You will see the light-sensor values update on the graph as you collect them.

After the program has finished running, disconnect the USB cable from the NXT and use the orange button on the NXT to run the program again. This time, explore the room looking for the highest and lowest light readings you can produce.

When you have taken thirty seconds of data, upload them to the computer using the upload button at the bottom right of the data-logging screen. The data set at the top of the list will be the one you just took. If you wish, you can collect additional data sets.

1. **What was the highest reading you found?**
Highest reading:

Where you found it:

2. **What was the lowest reading you found?**
Lowest reading:

Where you found it:

3. **Describe a problem that you encountered in doing this activity:**

4. **Describe something new that you learned or something interesting that you noticed:**

Teacher Information

Light and Dark Scavenger Hunt

This activity serves as an introduction to data logging. The students learn how to use a simple program to collect data.

Objectives
1. To write a simple data-logging program.
2. To learn how to collect and upload data.
3. To interpret the data on a graph.
4. To become familiar with the light sensor and its values.

Materials
NXT
Computer
Light sensor

Time: Approximately 30 minutes

Notes
1. Before doing this activity, demonstrate to the students how to create a new data-logging program.
2. Doing this lab before any of the following more complicated ones gives the students practice in logging data in a low-stakes lab where data runs can be easily repeated.
3. The students often show considerable ingenuity in registering high and low readings. At the finish of the activity, you may want to give the students a few minutes to share their favorite solutions with the rest of the class.
4. As an extension, the students can use temperature sensors to search for the highest and lowest temperatures.

Sample Program for Light and Dark Scavenger Hunt

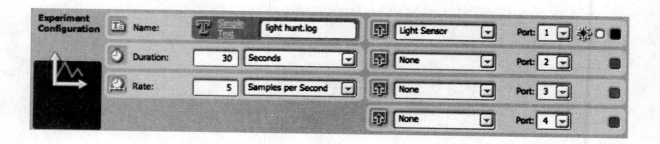

Answers to Light and Dark Scavenger Hunt

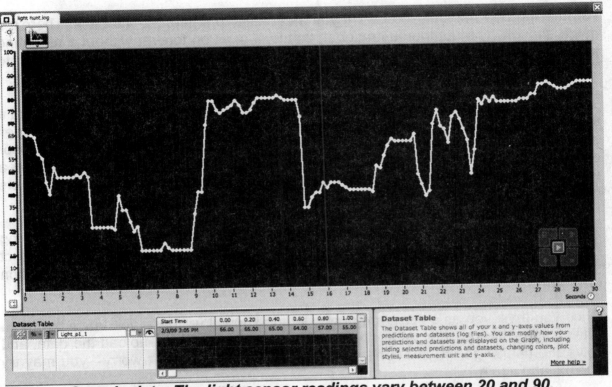

Sample data: The light sensor readings vary between 20 and 90.

1. **Answers will vary. Bright sunlight and projector bulbs are good sources of high readings.**
2. **Answers will vary. Obviously, dark rooms and closets are good sources of low readings.**
3. **Typical problems include confusing the various download buttons on the computer screen and mixing up data sets. Also, finding very low light readings can be difficult.**
4. **Answers will vary. Students are often struck by the intensity of sunlight and by the difficulty in obtaining very low numbers.**

I'm Thinking of a Number...

I'm thinking of a number and I want you as a class to figure out what it is. There's a catch, though. The number is irrational; that is, it goes on forever without a repeating pattern. One famous example of an irrational number is pi, which is equal to 3.14159265358...; another is the square root of 2, which is equal to 1.414213562....

To help you figure out the number, I will signal it to you using the NXTs. If you label a set of ten NXTs zero through nine, I will press a touch sensor on each in turn to spell out the number. For example, if my number were pi, I would press the touch sensor on the #3 NXT, then the #1 NXT, then #4, then #1 again, and so on. I will give you a total of ten digits. Notice that some digits may be used more than once and others may not be used at all.

To decipher the number, you will need to attach touch sensors to the NXTs and log them as I signal the number. As a group, you will need to decide how often to collect data points, how long to collect data for, and so on. Coordination and communication are vital!

Once you think you as a class are ready, let me know. I will have you leave the room while I signal the number. After I have finished, you may return, upload the data, and solve the challenge. (If you don't get it right the first time, don't worry—you may try again...and again.)

Teacher Information   I'm Thinking of a Number

This activity gives the students additional practice in using the data-logging program. To solve the puzzle, they must upload different data sets and then analyze the data.

Objectives
1. To be able to use the data-logging program.
2. To upload and analyze multiple data sets.
3. To work together as a group.

Materials
NXT
Computer
Touch sensor
Labels

Time: Approximately 40 minutes

Notes
1. If you use a square root as the irrational number (and tell the students that you are doing so), then they will be able to report the actual number to you. At the end of the activity, the students can punch the digits of the number into a calculator and square it to determine what irrational number you gave them.
2. Depending upon the group, you may want to assign roles to various students or leave the students to organize themselves.
3. If the students do not have experience organizing multiple data sets, you may want to demonstrate how to name the data sets and change the colors of the lines before starting this activity.

Sample Program for I'm Thinking of a Number

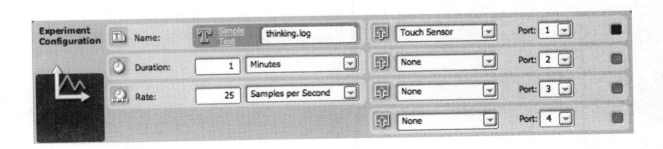

Answer to I'm Thinking of a Number

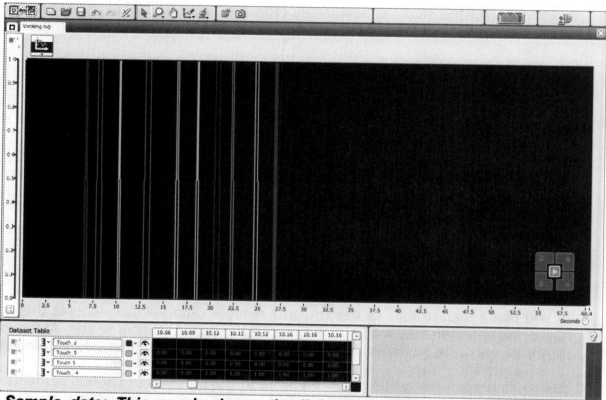

Sample data: This graph shows the light data taken by ten programmable bricks for the first ten digits of pi.

Thunderstorm

If you are near a thunderstorm, you can determine approximately how far away the storm is by counting the number of seconds between when you see the lightning flash and when you hear the thunder.

Here's why:
Light travels very quickly. In fact, the speed of light is 299,792,458 m/s. Even if the lightning flash is several kilometers away, you see it at practically the same instant as it occurs. However, sound travels much more slowly than light. The speed of sound is 340 m/s at sea level. So, if the thunder is several kilometers away, there is a delay between when it happens and when you hear it. You can use the difference between the speed of light and the speed of sound to estimate how far away a thunderstorm is.

1. In one second, how far can sound travel?

2. If you saw a flash of lightning and five seconds later heard the clap of thunder, approximately how far away would the storm be?

Now you will use your knowledge, along with data logging, to figure out how far away a simulated (fake!) storm is. Attach a light sensor to port 1 of your NXT and a sound sensor to port 2. Next, write a data-logging program to collect 10 samples per second for 20 seconds. Download the program to your NXT.

When everyone in the class is ready, the teacher will have you start your NXTs and take light and sound readings during a "thunderstorm." After the storm, upload your data to your NXT.

3. How many seconds apart did the lightning and thunder occur?

4. Approximately how far away was the storm?

Teacher Information   Thunderstorm

In this activity, the students log two different sensors at the same time.

Objectives
1. To gain additional practice in using data logging.
2. To learn how to log two different sensors at the same time.
3. To be able to analyze a graph containing multiple lines.

Materials
NXT
Computer
Light sensor
Sound sensor

Time: Approximately 20 minutes

Notes
1. To simulate lightning, you can turn the classroom lights on and off. For thunder, any loud, sudden sound—a dropped book, for example—will work.
2. The data for this lab can be collected either of two ways. The first method is to leave the NXT connected to the computer and have the data displayed in real time. The second way is to disconnect the NXT, collect the data, and then upload them afterwards.

Sample Program for Thunderstorm

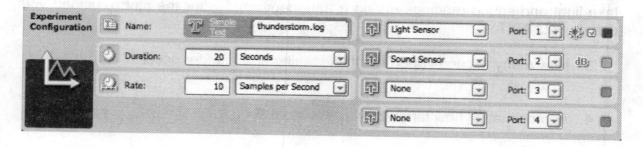

Answers to Thunderstorm

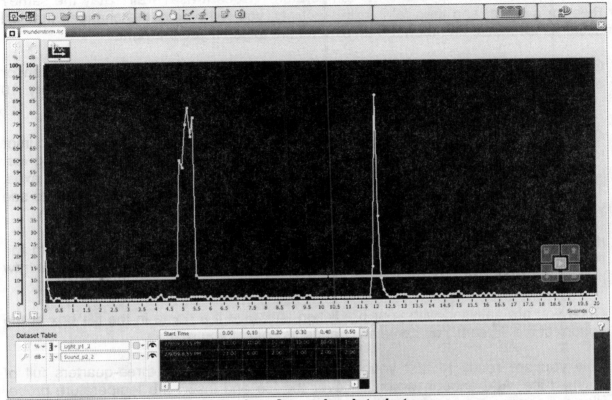

Sample data for a simulated storm.

1. In one second, sound can travel 1000m/340m = 2.94 kilometers, or approximately three km.
2. The storm would be around 15 km (= 5 s X 3 km/s) meters away.
3. Answers will vary. For the sample data, the lightning and thunder occurred about seven seconds apart.
4. Answers will vary. For the sample data, the storm was around 21 km away.

Melting

As ice melts, what happens to its temperature? Does it rise? Fall? Stay the same? Rise for a while, and then fall? In this activity, you will predict the changes that will occur as ice melts, and then run an experiment to see if you are right.

Open a new data-logging program. Set the program to record the temperature sensor on port 1 in degrees Celsius for 900 seconds, taking a data sample every 10 seconds.

On the top menu bar, choose the Prediction Tool and select pencil. Move your cursor to the graph and draw the temperature curve that you predict for the melting ice. Once you've drawn the curve, click on the icon in the lower left to change the axes. The axes will shift so that your curve covers the whole graph. Now it is easier to see your line.

If you want to make changes to what you've drawn, choose the eraser from the Prediction tool and move the cursor over the line you drew. The eraser will redraw that section of the line.

Once you are satisfied with your prediction line, give it a name in the file box at the bottom of the screen. You can also change its color if you wish.

Now you are ready to test your prediction. Fill a test tube three-quarters full of crushed ice. Add enough water to cover the ice and insert the temperature probe. Plug the sensor into port 1, put the test tube into a stand, and run the program.

When the program is finished, upload your data. Examine your data curve and your prediction curve.

1. Describe your data curve. Does it go up, down, up then down? Does the temperature change at a steady pace?

2. What are its maximum and minimum numbers?

3. How did your prediction compare to the actual data?

Teacher Information   Melting

In this activity, the students use the temperature sensor to record temperature changes during melting.

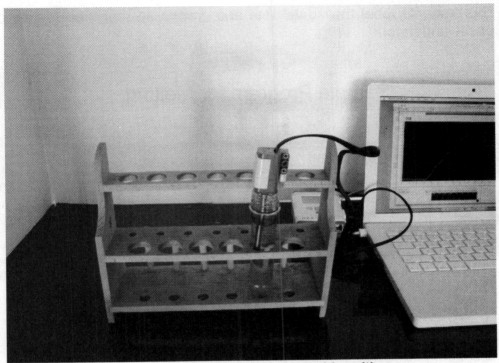

Using a test tube ensures rapid melting.

Objectives
1. To use the Prediction Tool.
2. To collect temperature data over time.

Materials
NXT
Computer
Temperature sensor
Test tube and stand
Crushed ice

Time: Approximately 40 minutes

Notes
1. Using crushed ice in water allows one to get usable results in fifteen minutes without an outside heat source. Alternatively, one could collect data for a longer period of time or apply a steady heat source to the test tube to speed melting.
2. Depending upon their familiarity with melting curves, the students may be able to

predict the melting plateau or they may assume that the temperature will increase at a steady rate.

3. The data for this lab can be collected either of two ways. The first method is to leave the NXT connected to the computer and have the data displayed in real time. The second way is to disconnect the NXT, collect the data, and then upload them afterwards.

4. Have the students label their data sets and graphs so that their results can be more easily understood.

Sample Program for Melting

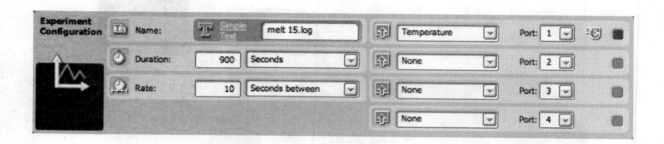

Answers to Melting

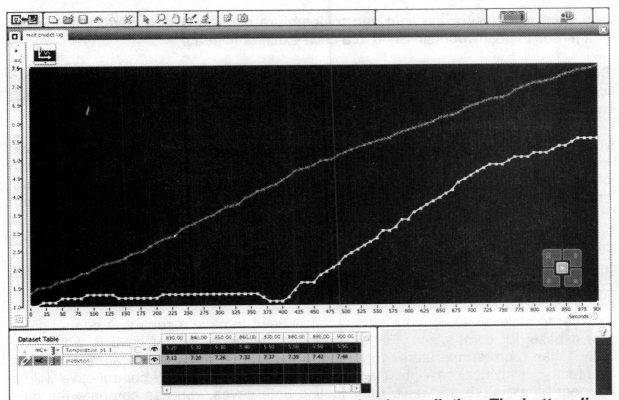

Sample data for Melting. The top line is a student's prediction. The bottom line is the actual data she collected.

1. Answers will vary. Most curves should have a plateau as the ice melts, followed by a more-or-less steady rise in temperature. Because the ice shifts within the test tube during melting, the students may see small fluctuations in the readings, though the overall trend should be an increase in temperature.
2. Answers will vary. For the sample data above, the minimum temperature was 1.00° C and the maximum was 5.50° C.
3. Answers will vary.

Cave Explorer

You want to measure the light and temperature conditions in a cave, but it is too dangerous to go in yourself. Send in a cave explorer instead.

Build a vehicle that will drive into a "cave," take sensor readings, and return. Use a light sensor to determine whether the cave is light or dark. Use a temperature sensor to determine if the cave is at room temperature, warmer, or colder.

Write a data-logging program to control your explorer and collect light and temperature data. Your explorer will start at a point one meter away from the mouth of the cave. It should drive into the cave (a large cardboard box), collect the data, and then return by driving backwards. To do this, you will need to combine data logging with motor control. Start by opening a new data-logging program. Set your light and temperature sensors in it. When you are done, choose Create Data Logging Program from the Tools menu. Your data-logging program will be turned into a block in an NXT Mindstorms program, to which you can add Move blocks to control your car.

In order to make sense of your data, you will need to have a control. A control gives you a basis for comparison. For example, to determine if your cave is warmer or colder than room temperature, you need to know what room temperature is. Before you test your mystery cave, test a similar cave as a control. The control cave will be at room temperature and unlit. After testing both caves, you can compare the data you took in each one.

1. What were the sensor readings in the dark, room-temperature control cave?

   Light:

   Temperature:

2. What were the sensor readings in the experimental cave?

   Light:

   Temperature:

3. What conditions do you think were present in the experimental cave? Justify your answers.

Teacher Information   Cave Explorer

This activity lets the students use many of the skills they have learned in the simpler data-logging activities.

An NXT with light and temperature sensors approaches the cave.

Objectives
1. To use data logging in a larger program involving movement.
2. To log two different sensors, light and temperature, at once.
3. To be able to analyze a graph containing multiple lines.

Materials
NXT
Computer
Motors
LEGO® pieces, including wheels
Light sensor
Temperature sensor
Cold and hot packs
Flashlights
Cardboard boxes to serve as caves

Time: Approximately 40 minutes

Notes

1. Before starting this activity, you will need to prepare at least two caves, the mystery cave and the control cave. To make each cave, cut a door in the side of large cardboard box for the NXT explorer to enter. Hang strips of paper or cloth over the opening so that the car can enter and exit, but the students cannot see into the cave.

2. Leave the control cave empty, so that the students will be able to take baseline readings for dark and for room temperature.

3. In the mystery cave, you may choose to place a lit flashlight and a cold or hot pack. Use tape to anchor them to the side of the cave.

4. You may want to include an unlit flashlight and a room-temperature hot/cold pack in the control cave to make the caves as similar as possible. Otherwise, the students may notice that if they bump them, one cave seems heavier than the other.

5. You may want to have several mystery caves, so that the students can try identifying various combinations of light and temperature.

6. As a class challenge, try having the class work together to identify several different caves, with each group allowed to make only a limited number of runs.

Sample Program for Cave Explorer

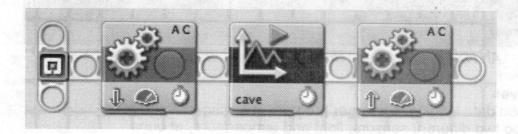

First Move block:

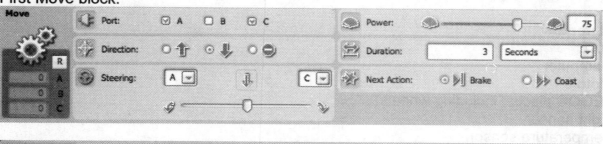

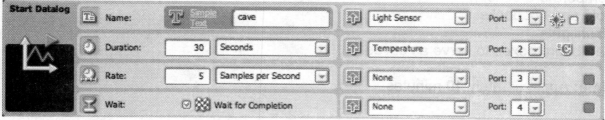

Second Move block:

Answers to Cave Explorer

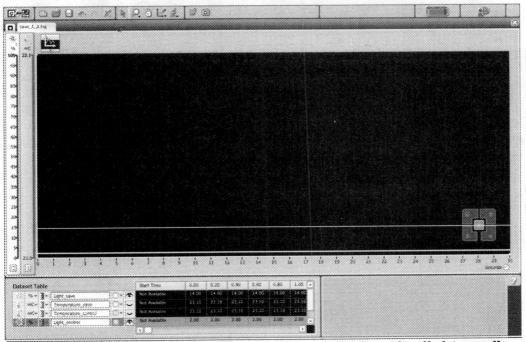

Sample light-sensor data for the cave, showing the light readings for the experimental (light) cave and the control (dark) cave.

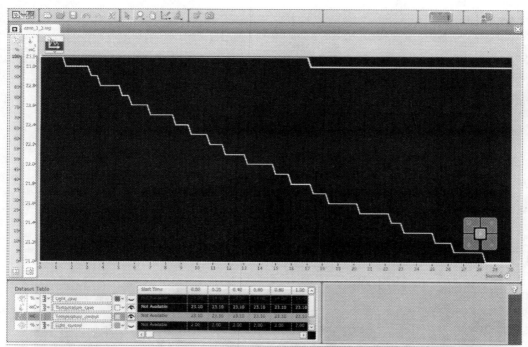

Sample temperature-sensor data for the cave, showing the temperature readings for the experimental (cold) cave and the control (room temperature) cave.

1. Answers will vary.
2. Answers will vary.
3. Answers will vary. The students should support their conclusions with data.

Part Seven: Physics Activities

These activities explore a number of different topics in physics, including velocity, forces, center of gravity, density, and heat transfer. The students gain a deeper understanding of the concepts by using them to solve problems. Along the way, the students are exposed to other important ideas, such as precision of measurement, experimental variables, and the engineering design process.

Several of the activities are projects, which challenge the students to apply what they have learned to design a solution to a problem. Others are data-logging activities, in which the students log sensors to gain additional insight into the concepts they are studying.

All of the activities require LEGO® materials. Many, but not all, of them require the NXT.

The activities in this section are:
1. Getting Up to Speed (Distance, Velocity, Graphing)
2. Stop for Pedestrians (Distance, Velocity)
3. Parking Space (Distance, Velocity, Graphing)
4. Crossing the Lines (Velocity, Acceleration)
5. Spinning your Wheels (Velocity, Rotation Speed, Graphing)
6. Zigzag and Diamond (Rotation Speed, Graphing)
7. No Wheels (Velocity, Friction)
8. Action-Reaction Car (Distance, Forces)
9. How Many Bricks in a Newton? (Forces, Mass, Weight)
10. Gear Training (Gears, Rotation Speed)
11. Worm Gears (Gears, Rotation Speed)
12. Spinning Colors (Gears, Rotation Speed, Light)
13. At a Snail's Pace (Velocity, Gears, Rotation Speed)
14. Perfect Pitcher (Distance, Projectile Motion, Levers)
15. Pulley Systems (Pulleys, Mechanical Advantage)
16. Ramp Up (Gears, Friction, Torque, Center of Gravity, Inclined Planes)
17. Peak Performance (Friction, Torque, Center of Gravity, Inclined Planes)
18. Balancing Nails (Center of Gravity, Stability, Equilibrium)
19. Tightrope Walker (Center of Gravity, Stability, Equilibrium)
20. LEGO Balance (Center of Gravity, Stability, Equilibrium, Torque)
21. Building Pressure (Pressure)
22. Floating LEGO Bricks (Mass, Volume, Density)
23. Cartesian Diver (Density, Pressure)
24. Stir It Up (Heat Transfer)
25. It's a Breeze (Heat Transfer)
26. Cool It Fast (Heat Transfer)
27. Hearing Test (Sound, Frequency)
28. Musical Instrument (Sound, Frequency)
29. Ultrasonic Pendulum NXT (Periodic Motion, Frequency)
30. Bright Light (Energy, Light, Torque, Wheels and Axles)

Getting Up to Speed

Build an NXT car and see how fast it goes.

First, construct a car that can travel more than two meters in a straight line. Program it to drive forward for a little more than two meters. Choose a motor power that moves your car at a moderate speed—something that you can easily time with a stopwatch.

Place your car behind the starting line. Start the program and then start the stopwatch as the car crosses the starting line. Stop timing when the car crosses the finish line. Record your results in the data table below. Run two more trials. Find the speed for each trial, plus average time and speed for the three trials.

Trial #	Distance (m)	Time (s)	Speed (m/s)
1	1 m		
2	1 m		
3	1 m		
Average	1 m		

1. What is the advantage of running more than one trial in this experiment?

2. How long do you think it will take your car to run 0.5 meters? Make a prediction, and then test it.

   Predicted time:

   Actual time:

3. How long do you think it will take your car to run 2.0 meters? Make a prediction and test it.

   Predicted time:

   Actual time:

4. How long do you think it will take your car to run 1.25 meters? Make a prediction and test it.

   Predicted time:

   Actual time:

5. Now, make a time vs. distance line graph of your data, graphing your average for one meter, plus your data for the other three distances.

   Here are some things to remember about graphs:
   ●Time (the independent variable) goes on the horizontal axis. Distance (the dependent variable) goes on the vertical axis.
   ●The units on each axis must be evenly spaced (so, in this case, your data points will not be evenly spaced).
   ●Each axis must be labeled and the graph must have a title.
   ●Accuracy and neatness are essential; color and attractiveness are nice, but optional.

Teacher Information

Getting Up to Speed

In this activity, the students build simple cars and time them to find their speeds over various distances.

Objectives
1. To build a simple and reasonably sturdy car
2. To calculate average speed from time and distance.
3. To use data to make predictions, then test them.
4. To make a line graph plotting time vs. distance.

Materials
NXT
Computer
Motors
LEGO® parts, including wheels
Tape for marking lines
Meter stick
Stopwatch

Time: Approximately 60 minutes

Notes
1. Before starting this activity, create a meter-long course for the cars with strips of tape for the start and finish. As the students do the activity, they will need to measure and add lines for 0.5 meters, 2.0 meters, and 1.25 meters.
2. If the students have had some experience with LEGO® materials, you can let them design and build their own cars. Alternatively, you can provide them with plans for a simple car. See the car-building plans in the Introductory Activities section for possible designs.
3. After the students have graphed their data, discuss the significance of the graph with them. Most of the students should find that their data points lie more or less in a straight line, as the speeds of the cars are generally constant. (Because the first data point was not taken until after the car was already moving, the acceleration of the car at the beginning will not appear on the graphs.) Discuss the possible reasons for any deviation from a straight line, both the possibility that the car's speed was not constant and the possibility of experimental error.
4. If the students are familiar with the concept of slope, have them compare the slope of the line on their graph with the average speed they calculated for the car.
5. As an extension, have the students run their cars at different motor powers and plot the data sets on the same graph. The resulting graph provides a nice illustration of the relationship between speed and slope. For a further exploration of this topic, see Spinning your Wheels.

Answers to Getting Up to Speed

Trial #	Distance (m)	Time (s)	Speed (m/s)
1	1 m	Answers will vary	Distance/Time
2	1 m	Answers will vary	Distance/Time
3	1 m	Answers will vary	Distance/Time
Average	1 m	Answers will vary	Average of the three speeds above

1. Taking the average of three runs usually improves the accuracy of your results by reducing the importance of any single error.
2. Predicted time: Answers will vary. Actual time: The time should be roughly half the time of the one-meter run.
3. Predicted time: Answers will vary. Actual time: The time should be roughly twice the time of the one-meter run.
4. Predicted time: Answers will vary. Actual time: The time should be roughly five-fourths the time of the one-meter run.
5. Graphs will vary. The line should be relatively straight, with its slope equal to the speed of the car.

Stop for Pedestrians

Pedestrians have the right of way. Can you program your car to stop for them?

A new pedestrian crosswalk is being planned for a two-meter-long road. Its exact location will be announced shortly. Before the crosswalk is constructed, you will be given some time to run your car for various distances along the road and collect data.

At the end of this practice time, the new pedestrian crosswalk will be built. You will be told exactly how far it is from the beginning of the road. You must program your car to drive as close as possible to the crosswalk without entering it. Once the crosswalk location is announced, you will not be allowed to run your car again. You may only program it.

For the test, you will place your car at the beginning of the road and, when given the signal, start the program. To successfully complete the challenge, your car must stop within ten centimeters of the crosswalk, but it must not knock over any minifigures in the crosswalk.

Good luck!

Teacher Information   Stop for Pedestrians

In this activity, the students run their cars over various distances and use the results to program the cars to go a specified distance.

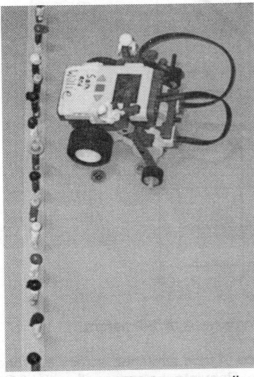

A car stops short of the crosswalk.

Objectives
1. To collect data to solve a particular problem
2. To use data to make predictions, then test them.
3. To interpolate from a line graph plotting time vs. distance.

Materials
NXT
Computer
Motors
LEGO® parts, including wheels
Tape for marking lines
Meter stick
Stopwatch
LEGO® minifigures

Time: Approximately 40 minutes

Notes
1. This activity is similar to the following one; the teacher should choose the version that is most appropriate for the class. Stop for Pedestrians has a shorter roadway, encourages the students to make a graph but does not require it, contains an element of competition, and may well result in LEGO minifigures being knocked over. Parking Space features a longer and more challenging roadway, requires the students to make a data table and graph, and does not involve direct competition or potential injury to minifigures.
2. Before starting this activity, create a two-meter-long course for the cars with strips of tape for the start and finish.

3. Depending upon the students, you may want to give them some guidance in collecting data and encourage them to graph their results.

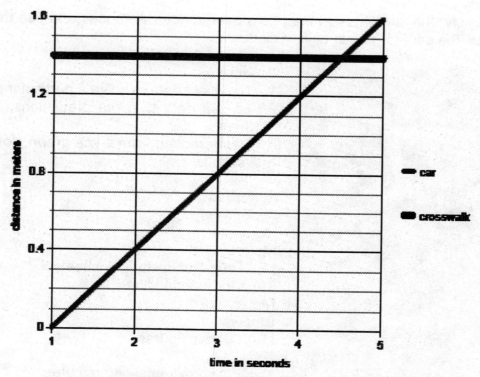

A graph of sample data, showing a crosswalk at 1.4 meters.

4. The crosswalk can be made from a long piece of tape stretched across the road. Make sure that it is parallel to the starting line. Populate the crosswalk with LEGO minifigures.
5. The assessment for this activity can be accomplished in different ways. One way is to require any students who are not successful to repeat the challenge, with different crosswalk locations, until they pass it. Another way is to note each group's results on the initial test and then give prizes—a small prize to any group which comes within ten centimeters of the crosswalk without going over; a slightly larger prize to the group that comes closest without going over.

Acknowledgement

This activity is based upon one by Professor Chris Rogers of Tufts University.

Parking Space

It is a long-standing tradition in some neighborhoods of Boston to dig the snow out of a parking space after a snowstorm and then save the space with traffic cones, lawn chairs, or other objects.

Such a parking space has been saved for you. All you have to do is park in it.

You will have time to practice driving on the three-meter-long street. You may use this time to try driving various distances and times. What you try is up to you; the only rule is that you must make a table and a graph of your data.

At the end of the practice time, you will be told exactly where your parking space is. After you are told, you may program your car, but you may not run it.

After all of the cars are programmed, we will run them one by one and see which ones are able to park entirely within the space.

Good luck!

Teacher Information

Parking Space

In this activity, the students run their cars over various distances and use the results to program the cars to go a specified distance.

The students time their cars on a practice roadway.

Objectives
1. To collect data to solve a particular problem
2. To use data to make predictions, then test them.
3. To interpolate from a line graph plotting time vs. distance.

Materials
NXT
Computer
Motors
LEGO® parts, including wheels
Tape for marking lines
Meter stick
Stopwatch

Time: Approximately 40 minutes

Notes

1. This activity is similar to the previous one; the teacher should choose the version that is most appropriate for the class. Stop for Pedestrians has a shorter roadway, encourages the students to make a graph but does not require it, contains an element of competition, and may well result in LEGO® minifigures being knocked over. Parking Space features a longer and more challenging roadway, requires the students to make a data table and graph, and does not involve direct competition or potential injury to minifigures.

2. Before starting this activity, create a three-meter-long course for the cars with strips of tape for the start and finish.

3. Depending upon the students, you may want to give them some guidance in collecting data and graphing their results.

4. This activity can be made easier or harder by adjusting the size of the parking space. A thirty-centimeter-long space provides a challenge but will allow most students to be successful.

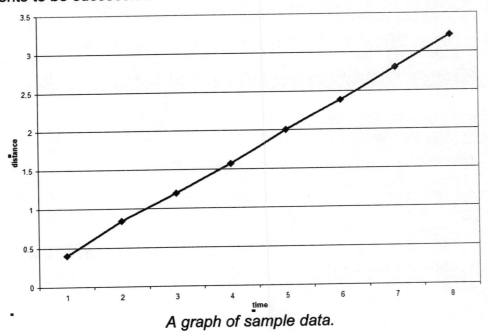

A graph of sample data.

Crossing the Lines

Use a light sensor to investigate the motion of your car.

Build an NXT vehicle and attach a light sensor to it. The light sensor should be on the front of the vehicle, fairly close to the floor and pointing downward.

Write a program to log the light sensor as your car moves. Take twenty light-sensor reading per second. Turn on motors A and C at a power level low enough so that your vehicle does not cross the tape lines too quickly. Run the motors long enough that the car crosses the final line before stopping.

Place your car with the light sensor just behind the starting line. Start the program running and let the vehicle take data.

Return to your computer and upload the data you have collected.

1. How can you tell when your car crossed each line?

2. Does your car accelerate? How do you know?

3. Calculate your vehicle's average speed over the 2.00-meter track. Be sure to show your work.

4. What possible sources of error exist in this experiment? Make a list.

Teacher Information

Crossing the Lines

In this activity, the students use light sensors to measure the speed of their cars, by running the cars over a striped course and analyzing the minima created in the light-sensor output as the cars cross the dark lines.

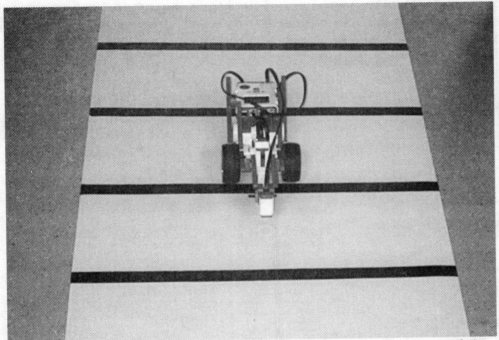

An NXT car with a light-sensor mounted on the front collects data.

Objectives
1. To use a light sensor and data logging to analyze speed and acceleration.
2. To calculate average speed from time and distance.
3. To interpret a graph to see when the car was accelerating or decelerating.

Materials
NXT
Computer
Light sensor
Motors
LEGO® parts, including wheels
Tape and meter stick for constructing the course

Time: Approximately 40 minutes

Notes
1. Before starting this activity, create a two-meter-long course for the cars. The

course should consist of a light-colored background, with a strip of dark tape placed every 20 cm along it. (You can also use light tape on a dark background; the resulting light-intensity measurements will show a maximum for each tape line rather than a minimum.)

2. The students can build cars from plans or construct their own designs. See the simple cars in the Introductory Activities section for possible designs.

3. In order to make the graph easier to decipher, you may want to mark the beginning and end of the track with sheets of dark paper rather than lines.

4. Some students may need help in analyzing the graph. In particular, they may need help in making the connection between wider spacing of the minima and slower speed.

Sample Program for Crossing the Lines

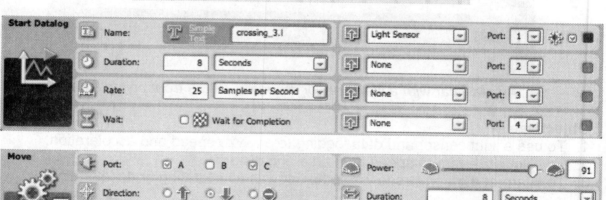

Answers to Crossing the Lines

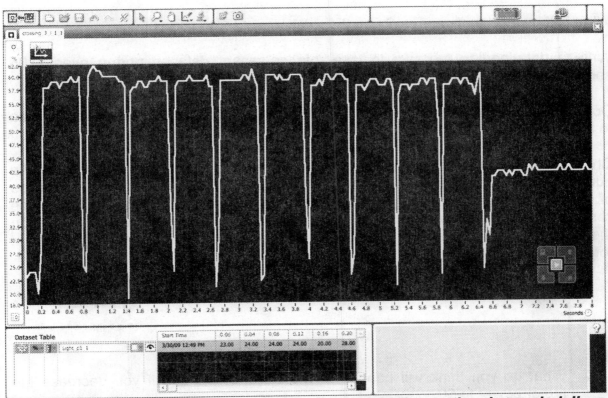

Sample data: Eleven minima are visible, corresponding to the eleven dark lines on the track.

1. The light-sensor graph shows a minimum (valley) whenever a line is crossed (or a peak, if light tape is used).
2. Answers will vary. After a brief initial period of acceleration, most cars will show a constant speed. If the valleys are evenly spaced, then the car is traveling at a constant speed. If the valleys get closer together, then the car is speeding up. If the space between valleys grows wider, then the car is slowing down.
3. Answers will vary. To calculate the average speed for a run, divide 2.00 meters by the time elapsed between when the car crosses the starting line and when it crosses the finish line. For the sample data shown in the graph, the average speed is 0.3 m/s.
4. Possible sources of error include: the track is not exactly 2.00 meters long, the tape lines are not evenly spaced, the car does not travel in a straight line, the light sensor misses a tape line between logging points, the times are not read off the graph correctly, the calculations are not performed correctly.

Spinning your Wheels

What is the velocity of your car? Log the rotation sensor to find out.

Write a data-logging program to take rotation-sensor data on port A every 0.05 seconds for ten seconds, while running the motors at 75% power.

Download your program to the NXT. Run the car and upload the rotation-sensor data to the computer.

Choose Analysis Tools from the menu bar. Click on the box that says Linear Fit. An equation will be displayed, the equation of the line that best fits your data. The slope of the line (the coefficient of x in the equation) tells you how many units the line changes vertically for every unit it changes horizontally. In this case, it is telling you the number of rotations every second—in other words, the speed of the car in rotations per second.

1. What is the speed of your car in rotations/second?

2. What do you think will happen to the slope of the line if you decrease the motor power to 50%?

3. Decrease the motor power to 50% and run the car again. What is the new slope—that is, the speed in rotations/second?

4. What do you think will happen if you increase the power to 100%?

5. Try it and see. What is the speed in rotations/second of the car running at full power?

Now, calculate the velocity in meters per second of the car running at full power. To do this, you need to know how far the car travels with each complete rotation of the wheels. Use a marker to draw a heavy ink line across the tread of the tire. (If your car has more than one size of wheels, make sure you use the wheel attached to the rotation sensor.) Roll the car across a piece of paper. The inked wheel should leave a mark each time the ink line rolls over the paper. Measure the distance between two successive lines in meters to find the distance per rotation. Notice that you've just found the circumference of the tire. Multiply your full-power velocity in rotations/second by the tire circumference to obtain the velocity in meters/second.

6. What is the circumference of your tire?

7. What is the velocity of your car in meters/second?

Teacher Information   Spinning your Wheels

In this activity, the students use rotation sensors to analyze the speed of their cars, making use of the Analysis Tools to fit a line to their data.

This two-motor car uses the NXT at an angle.

Objectives
1. To use a rotation sensor and data logging to analyze velocity.
2. To use the Analysis Tools area to fit a line to a set of data.
3. To interpret a slope in an equation and on a graph.

Materials
NXT
Computer
Motor
LEGO® parts, including wheels
Marker

Time: Approximately 40 minutes

Notes
1. If the students have NXT cars from the previous activity, they can use them for this activity as well. For possible designs for the car, see the building plans in the

Introductory Activities section.

2. Depending upon the students' background in mathematics, you may want to introduce or review equations of lines and slope with them at the start of this activity.

3. If the car produces downward sloping lines because of the way the motors are oriented, it can be run backwards for this activity.

Sample Program for Spinning your Wheels

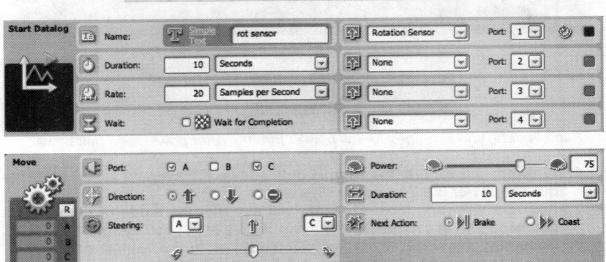

Answers to Spinning your Wheels

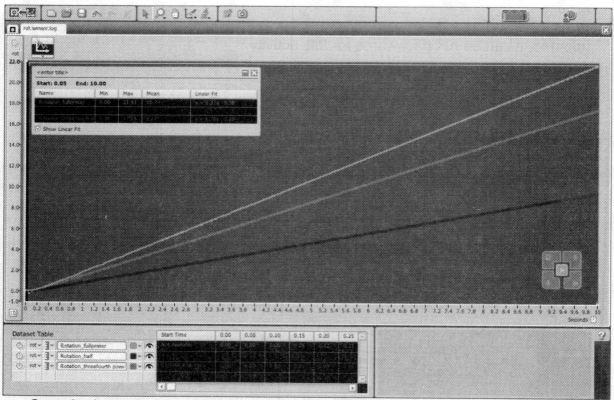

Sample data, showing lines for full power, three-quarter power, and half power.

1. **Answers will vary. In the sample data above, the average speed at three-quarter power is 1.78 rotations/second.**
2. **Answers will vary. Most students will say that the slope of the line will decrease (but accept other ideas, since they are speculating).**
3. **Generally, the slope of the line will decrease. In the sample data above, the average speed at half power is 0.97 rotations/second.**
4. **Most students will say that the slope will increase.**
5. **The slope should increase. In the sample data above, the average speed at full power is 2.22 rotations/second. The increase or decrease will not necessarily be directly proportional to the motor power, though the slope will increase as the power increases.**
6. **Answers will vary, depending upon the tire used.**
7. **Answers will vary. For the sample data shown above, the average velocity was 0.40 m/s, based upon a tire circumference of 0.18 m and a slope of 2.22 rotations/second in the equation.**

Zigzag and Diamond

A two-motor NXT car was run with the rotation sensor in each motor being logged. Here is the resulting graph. (The two lines, one for each motor, are on top of one another.)

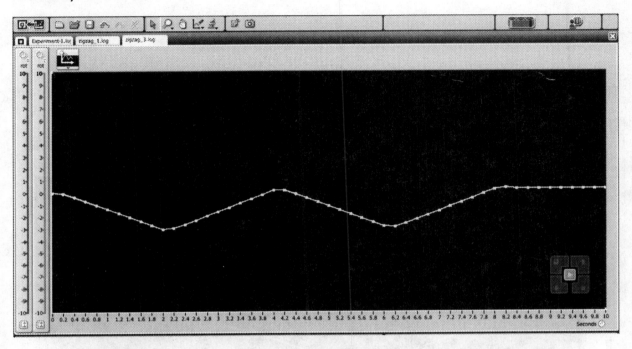

1. How do you think the car was moving during each section of the graph?
    a. First section, downhill line:

    b. Second section, uphill line:

    c. Third section, downhill line:

    d. Fourth section, uphill line:

2. Try programming your car to mimic this graph. Download and run the program. How close did you come?

3. Modify your program until the graphs match. Describe your final program.

The car was run again, producing the following graph:

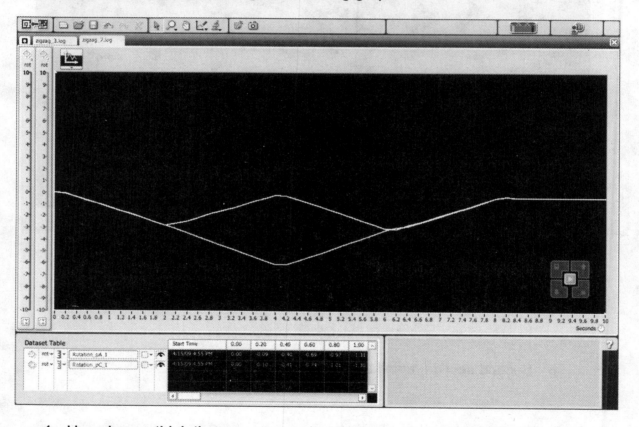

4. How do you think the car was moving during each section of this graph?
   a. First section, downhill line:

   b. Second section, first half of diamond:

c. Third section, second half of diamond:

d. Fourth section, uphill line:

5. Write a program to mimic this graph. Describe your program.

6. Run your program and modify it if necessary to match the graph. Describe your final program.

Teacher Information   Zigzag and Diamond

In this activity, the students analyze rotation-sensor graphs, working backward to generate the motion of the car from the graph.

Objectives
1. To use a rotation sensor and data logging to analyze motion.
2. To interpret and reproduce a graph.

Materials
NXT
Computer
Motors
LEGO® parts, including wheels

Time: Approximately 40 minutes

Notes
1. Depending upon how the motors are oriented, the increasing slope may correspond to the actual car moving forward or moving backward. On the answer sheet, an uphill slope corresponds to forward motion.
2. As an extension, you can have the students write their own programs to generate mystery graphs, and then have them try to solve their classmates' graphs.

Sample Program for Zigzag and Diamond

Data-logging block:

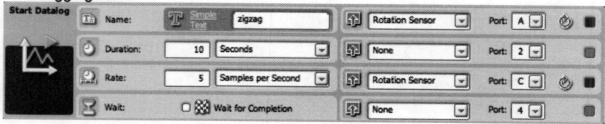

Zigzag program:

Each of the first four Move blocks runs for two seconds.

Diamond program:

Each of the first four Move blocks runs for two seconds.

Answers to Zigzag and Diamond

1. The zigzag pattern, section by section. (Note: depending upon the orientation of the car's motors, the directions may be reversed; in other words, the car would move forward first, then backward.)
    a. First section, downhill line: Car drives backward for two seconds.
    b. Second section, uphill line: Car drives forward for two seconds.
    c. Third section, downhill line: Car drives backward for two seconds.
    d. Fourth section, uphill line: Car drives forward for two seconds.

2-3. Initial answers may vary. The final program should be similar to the one below.

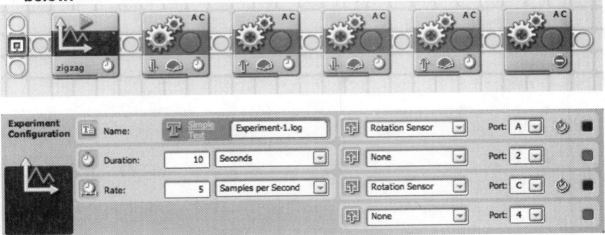

4. The diamond pattern, section by section. (Note: depending upon the orientation of the car's motors, the directions may be reversed; in other words, the car would move forward first, then backward.)
    e. First section, downhill line: Car drives backward for two seconds.
    f. Second section, first half of diamond: Car turns counterclockwise for two seconds.
    g. Third section, second half of diamond: Car turns clockwise for two seconds.
    h. Fourth section, uphill line: Car drives forward for two seconds.

5-6. Initial answers may vary. The final program should be similar to the one below.

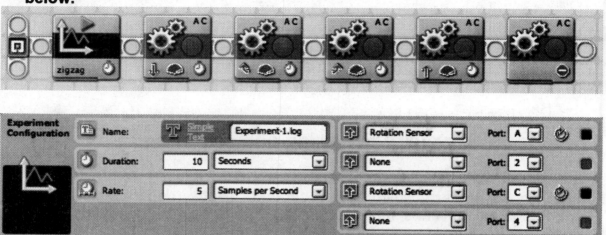

No Wheels

Build an NXT creature that moves. It may hop, squirm, crawl, whatever you like. However, it may not have wheels of any type.

1. Describe and sketch the mechanism you used to make your creature move.

2. Describe a design change you made as you were building and testing your creature. How did this change affect the creature's movement?

3. How fast does your creature move? Use a meter stick and a timer to calculate its speed in centimeters per second.

Examples of Legs

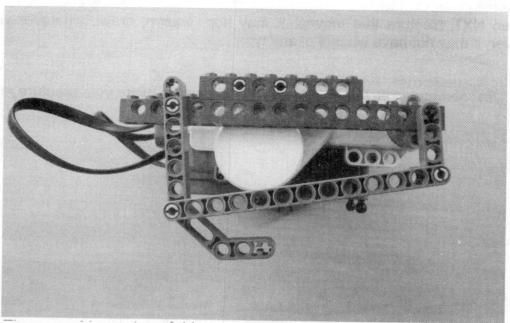

The curved-beam leg of this creature is connected to the motor by a four-bar linkage.

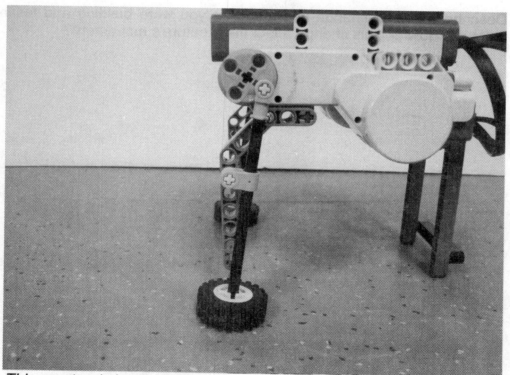

This creature's leg is an axle mounted off-center on the motor. Its high center of gravity makes it less stable than the preceding example.

Teacher Information   No Wheels

The students design creatures that move without using wheels.

This scorpion moves by means of rotating beams attached directly to the motors.

Objectives
1. To design a robotic creature that moves without wheels.
2. To use a meter stick and timer to calculate the speed of a moving object.

Materials
NXT
Computer
Motors
LEGO® pieces
Meter stick
Timer

Time: Approximately 80 minutes

Notes

1. Tell the students that they may use tires, though not as wheels. Tires positioned flat against the ground make excellent feet.
2. This activity provides an opportunity to discuss friction, as many of the initial foot designs will probably have trouble gaining enough traction to move the NXT forward.
3. Encourage trial and error. After some experimentation, the students will begin to see what types of designs are successful in producing movement. You may want to have the students share some of their more successful designs with the rest of the class to expand the range of possibilities.
4. The motion of the creatures may be jerky and non-linear. You may want to discuss how this irregular motion complicates the calculation of the speed. Point out that the average speed may actually encompass a range of speeds.

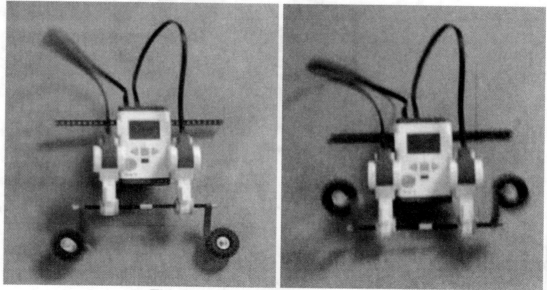

This hopping car uses tires as feet.

Answers to No Wheels

1. **Answers will vary.**
2. **Answers will vary.**
3. **Answers will vary.**

Action/Reaction Car

For every action, there is an equal and opposite reaction. For example, you can power a vehicle by attaching an inflated balloon to it. As air escapes out the back of the balloon, the vehicle is pushed forward.

Use this principle, Newton's third law of motion, to make a balloon-powered car that will travel as far as possible. Your car must be constructed of LEGO® pieces and one balloon. You will make sketches of the initial and final versions of your car. After each trial, you will record how the car performed, one problem you encountered, and what modification(s) you will make before the next trial.

Starter car:
Sketch:

Distance traveled:

Something that worked well:

Problem encountered:

Change to be made:

Second trial:
Distance traveled:

Something that worked well:

Problem encountered:

Change to be made:

Third trial:
Distance traveled:

Something that worked well:

Problem encountered:

Change to be made:

Continue to test and improve your car. At the end, make a sketch of your final car and note the farthest distance it traveled.

Final car:
Sketch:

Distance traveled:

Teacher Information   Action-Reaction Car

The students build balloon-powered cars.

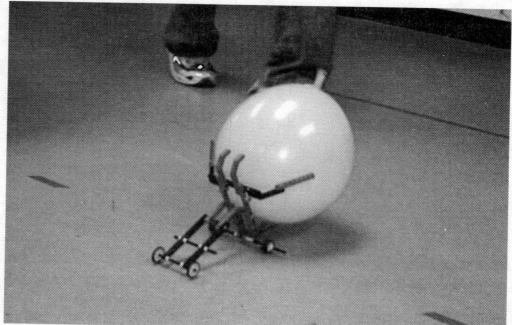

In this clever design, the balloon that propels the car is not attached to it. Instead, the balloon is cradled in a frame.

Objectives
1. To design and build a balloon-powered car that demonstrates action and reaction forces.
2. To use the engineering design process.
3. To modify a design one step at a time.

Materials
LEGO® pieces
Balloons
Meter stick

Time: Approximately 90 minutes

Notes
1. Like a rocket, the balloon-powered car demonstrates Newton's third law: For every action, there is an equal and opposite reaction.
2. You can either give the students one type of balloon or let them experiment with different shapes and sizes. Twelve-inch round balloons work well.
3. Encourage the students to follow the instructions on the handout, making only one change at a time and then evaluating it. Many of the students will be tempted

to implement several of their ideas at once. Point out to them that it will be much harder to determine the effect of each modification if they have made several changes at once. On the other hand, allow the students some leeway if they want to abandon their design and try a new one. Some of them will find that their first ideas do not work at all.

4. One of the biggest challenges in this activity is designing the frame that holds the end of the balloon so that it lets air out at a steady rate, not too fast and not too slow. The gear box performs this function well. The end of the balloon can be threaded thought the opening where the worm gear usually sits.

5. If the students are at a loss for changes to try, suggest that they experiment with different tires. Switching the tires can have a significant effect on the car's performance.

A balloon-powered car on a test run.

How Many Bricks in a Newton?

If you had a newton of two-stud-by-four-stud LEGO® bricks, how many bricks would you have?

   1. Make a guess (It does not matter whether you are correct.).

In this lab, you will figure out just how many LEGO bricks are in a newton.

First, find out how much the mass of a LEGO brick varies from one brick to another. Mass five LEGO bricks, one at a time. Record your results in the table below.

Brick number	Mass in grams
1	
2	
3	
4	
5	
Average	

   2. Use the data that you collected to calculate how many LEGO bricks are in a newton. Write an explanation of your reasoning, showing the calculations that you performed and justifying each one.

Teacher Information   How Many Bricks in a Newton?

This activity gives the students a better sense of how large a newton is. It also gives them practice in using the relationship F = ma to convert grams to newtons.

Objectives
1. To use a balance.
2. To gain an understanding of the size of a newton.
3. To learn the difference between mass and weight and how to find one from the other.
4. To explain the reasoning behind a set of calculations.

Materials
Balance, preferably precise to at least hundredths of a gram
2 x 4 LEGO® bricks

Time: Approximately 40 minutes

Notes
1. A 2 x 4 LEGO brick has a mass of around 2.2 grams, so there are roughly 45 bricks in a newton.
2. The students should be taught to use the balance before beginning this lab.
3. The students should be familiar with mass, weight, and Newton's second law before doing this lab.
4. You may want to discuss two different methods of finding the average mass of the bricks—massing them one at a time as in this activity or massing all five together. Massing the five together will reduce the error in massing (since you are massing once instead of five times), but it does not give you an idea of how much the mass varies from brick to brick.
5. If the students are familiar with the concept of significant figures, this activity is a good place to discuss them.

Answers to How Many Bricks in a Newton?

1. **Answers will vary.**

    Sample data:

Brick number	Mass in grams
1	2.22
2	2.22
3	2.19
4	2.22
5	2.19
Average	2.21

2. **The average mass of the five bricks was 2.21 grams. In order to convert the mass to kilograms, divide by 1000. So, the mass in kilograms is 0.00221. To find the weight of one brick in newtons, multiply the mass in kilograms by the acceleration due to gravity, 9.8 m/s/s.**

    (0.00221 kg) (9.8 m/s/s) = 0.022 newtons.

    Since each brick weighs an average of 0.0022 newtons, divide one newton by this average weight to determine how many bricks are in a newton:

    1/ (0.022) = 45.

    There are approximately 45 LEGO® bricks in one newton.

Gear Training: Exploring the Basics of Gears

First, some terms: Two or more gears meshed together are called a **gear train**. The gear to which the force is initially applied is called the **driver**. The final gear is called the **follower**, or **driven gear**. Any gears between the driver and the follower are called **idlers**.

Now, try building each of the trains described below. Sketch or list the gears you used for each. (Some useful information--the smallest LEGO® spur gear has eight teeth, the medium gear has twenty-four teeth, and the largest has forty teeth.)

1. The driver and the follower turn at the same speed, but in opposite directions.

2. The driver and the follower turn at the same speed in the same direction.

3. The driver turns three times as fast as the follower.

4. The follower turns five times as fast as the driver.

5. The follower turns twenty-five times as fast as the driver. (There's a trick to this one!)

Gearing up and gearing down: **Gearing up** means that the follower in a particular gear train turns faster than the driver. **Gearing down** means that the follower turns more slowly than the driver.

6. Look back at the gear trains you made. For each one, note whether it was gearing up, gearing down, or neither.

Teacher Information   Gear Training

The students explore gears, building gear trains and learning about ratios, gearing up, and gearing down.

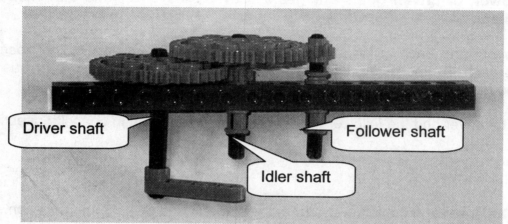

The eight-tooth follower in this gear train turns twenty-five times faster than the driver and its crank.

Objectives
1. To build a variety of gear trains.
2. To calculate gear ratios.
3. To understand gearing up and gearing down.

Materials
LEGO® parts, including gears

Time: Approximately 30 minutes

Notes
1. Provide long beams, axles, bushings, and a variety of gears for each group.
2. The eight-, twenty-four-, and forty-tooth gears work well for this activity because they can be easily meshed along a single beam. The sixteen-tooth gears cannot because of the spacing of the holes along the beam.

Answers to Gear Training:
Exploring the Basics of Gears

1. Any two gears of the same size, meshed together, will turn at the same speed but in opposite directions. For example, two forty-tooth gears. (Neither gearing up nor gearing down)

2. Any two gears of the same size, with an idler between them, will turn at the same speed and in the same direction. For example, two forty-tooth gears with an eight-tooth gear between them. (Neither gearing up nor gearing down)

3. Any gear train where the follower is three times as large as the driver will make the driver turn three times as fast as the follower. For example, an eight-tooth gear meshed with a twenty-four-tooth gear. (Gearing down)

4. Any gear train where the driver is five times as large as the follower will make the follower turn five times as fast as the driver. For example, a forty-tooth gear meshed with an eight-tooth gear. (Gearing up)

5. A gear train with stacked gears on an idler shaft will allow the follower to turn twenty-five times as fast as the driver, as illustrated in the picture at the beginning of the Teacher Information page. The first axle holds a forty-tooth gear. The second axle contains two gears, an eight-tooth gear meshed with the large gear on the first axle and a forty-tooth gear. The forty-tooth gear on the second axle is meshed with an eight-tooth gear on the third axle. Each pair of gears increase the speed by five times, so the two pairs together give an increase of twenty-five times. (Gearing up)

6. The answers are given in parentheses after each of the above questions.

Worm Gears

A worm gear has a different shape than other gears you have seen. It is shaped like a corkscrew. Let's investigate how it works.

Place a 24-tooth gear and a worm gear in a gear box. Place axles through each one and secure the worm-gear axle with bushings. Attach a crank to each axle.

1. Try turning the crank attached to the worm gear. How many times must you turn it in order for the 24-tooth gear to make one complete rotation?

2. Examine a worm gear carefully. How many teeth does it have?

3. Now try turning the crank attached to the 24-tooth gear. How many times must you turn it to make the worm gear turn once?

4. Construct a gear train with a slowdown of 72 times—the driver must turn 72 times in order for the follower to turn once. Make a sketch of your gear train.

Teacher Information

Worm Gears

This activity introduces the students to worm gears.

If a gear box is not available, a frame of beams and plates can be used to mesh the worm gear and the spur gear.

Objectives
1. To learn how to use a worm gear.
2. To build compound gear trains.

Materials
Gear box (or beams and plates)
Worm and spur gears
LEGO® pieces

Time: Approximately 30 minutes

Notes
1. This activity lets the students experiment with worm gears.
2. The handout includes a trick question—the third one. The students are asked to turn the crank on the spur gear in order to turn the worm gear. Of course, since the worm gear is a one-way gear, the gears lock rather than turning. Trying it for

themselves helps the concept to register more than if the students are simply told that a worm gear cannot be used for gearing up.

Answers to Worm Gears

1. **The worm gear must turn 24 times in order for the 24-tooth gear to make one complete rotation.**
2. **A worm gear has only one tooth, which spirals the length of the gear.**
3. **This is a trick question. The 24-tooth gear cannot be turned. The worm gear can only be used for gearing down.**
4. **Attach the gear box to a gear train containing an 8-tooth driver and a 24-tooth follower.**

Spinning Colors

Build a gear train where the follower rotates 25 times faster than the driver. Cut out one of the disks from the design sheet and glue it to thin cardboard. Mount the disk above the follower, anchoring it to the axle with bushings.

1. Now spin the driver at varying speeds and watch the disk. What colors do you see?

A number of black-and-white patterns fool your eye into seeing flashes of color when they are spun. Try the other design, and then invent your own pattern.

2. Sketch any of your invented patterns that produce colors.

3. Make a gear train in which the follower spins 125 times faster than the driver. Use it to spin your disk. What happens?

4. Divide a circle into eight equal wedges. Leave one white and color the other seven the colors of the rainbow: red, orange, yellow, green, blue, indigo, violet. Spin the circle. What do you see?

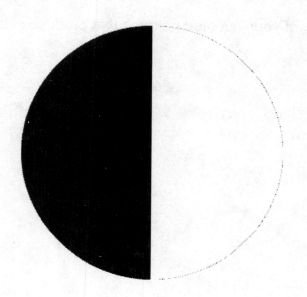

Teacher Information   Spinning Colors

The students use gears to spin Benham's disks.

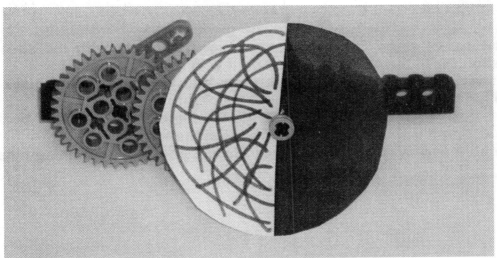

A student-made Benham's disk.

Objectives
1. To build a gear train in which the follower moves 25 times faster than the driver.
2. To experiment with Benham's disks and the color spectrum.

Materials
LEGO® pieces
Thin cardboard
Scissors
Glue
Markers
Compasses for making circles

Time: Approximately 30 minutes

Notes
1. This activity makes a good follow-up activity to Gear Training. The students who finish Gear Training quickly will have more time to design their own Benham's disks.
2. The third template, the half-black/half-white disk, can be used for the students' own designs.
3. Benham was a toymaker in the 1800's who discovered this illusion while experimenting with tops. The effect is produced by differences in the cones of your eyes. You have three types of cones, one for detecting blue light, one for red, and one for green. The three types of cones have different response

patterns, so that the flashes of white light on the spinning disk activate them in different ways. Their varying responses create the illusion of color.

Answers to Spinning Colors

1. **Answers will vary. Often, the colors seen will vary with the speed of rotation. Have the students experiment with different speeds.**
2. **Answers will vary. Generally, patterns that are at least half black and contain thin black arcs are the most successful.**
3. **This gear train will be difficult, if not impossible, to turn because increasing the speed of the gears reduces the torque.**
4. **The spinning rainbow will produce a white color (or something close to it).**

At a Snail's Pace

Now that you know about velocity and gears, it is time for a snail race. As you know, snails are very slow. In fact, in this race, the slowest snail wins.

Here are the rules:

•Your snail must include an NXT, one or two motors, and one or more gear trains. You may also use craft materials, such as pipe cleaners and tissue paper, for decoration.

•Your snail must move forward at a constant pace during the race, though its forward motion can be very slow. In other words, no stopping, no turning, and no backing up.

•Your snail must look like a snail.

Once your snail is complete, document it:

•Calculate the slowdown—how many times your motor must turn in order for your wheels to turn once.

•Make a careful schematic of your gear train, showing how the gears mesh with one another. Your drawing does not need to be realistic; you may use symbols to represent the various sizes of gears. Be sure to include a key.

Good luck and may the slowest snail win!

Teacher Information

At a Snail's Pace

The students build snails for a snail race, where the slowest snail wins. This activity gives the students experience in building and analyzing complicated gear trains.

The motor of this very long NXT snail must turn 5.3 x 10^{44} times in order for the wheels to turn once.

Objectives
1. To gain practice using gear trains, including compound gears and worm gears.
2. To be able to calculate gear ratios for complicated gear trains.
3. To design a gear train with its overall appearance and dimensions in mind (so that the result will look like a snail).

Materials
NXT
Computer
Motors
LEGO® pieces, including gears
Decorative materials
Tape for starting line

Time: Approximately 90 minutes

Notes
1. Before doing this activity, be sure that the students are introduced to compound gears and worm gears.
2. If you do not have access to a large supply of gears, you may want to set limits on how many gears each group may use.
3. Though this activity is billed as a race, try to de-emphasize the competitive aspects. In reality, many of the snails will be so slow that it will be nearly impossible to determine a winner.
4. You may want to add an additional constraint that the students must demonstrate that their snail moves forward, at least in theory, rather than moving backward (a real possibility, given the complexity of the gear trains).

A Snail and its Schematic

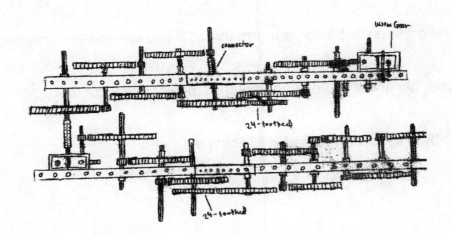

≡ = 40-toothed gear

≡ = 24-toothed gear

▥ = 8-toothed gear

Snail Car Gear Train

Speed: The motor must turn

9,765,624,992,000 times
for the tread to turn
JUST ONCE!

Perfect Pitcher

Build a motorized pitching arm. Can you design an arm that can throw the ball a long distance? Can you design an arm that can throw the ball accurately? An arm that can do both?

The design you use is up to you, but your contraption must contain a lever, a motor, and a touch sensor to start the motor. The motor may be used to power the arm directly or to prepare it. For example, you could use the motor to wind a rubber band, which you then release to activate the arm.

There will be contests for distance and for accuracy. You may choose to enter either or both of the contests.

For each contest, the ball must start behind the tape line. However, the NXT itself may be in front of the line. You may place the pitching arm however you wish, as long as the part holding the ball is behind the line.

Distance scoring: The distance will be measured from the starting line to the spot where the ball first hits the ground. You will get three tries; the best score of the three will count.

Accuracy scoring: The accuracy target will consist of a cup glued to a plate. Throwing the ball into the inner cup earns three points. Touching the inner cup earns two points. Throwing into the outer plate earns one point. You will get three throws; your accuracy score is the cumulative score for the three throws.

1. List the greatest distance your arm threw, if you entered the distance contest.

2. List your accuracy score, if you entered the accuracy contest.

3. Describe a success you had in building your arm.

4. Describe a difficulty you encountered in building your arm.

5. Make a sketch of your pitching arm. Tell whether it is a first, second, or third class lever. Identify the fulcrum, load (output force), and effort force (input force).

6. Some levers are used to magnify the force. In this case, that would mean that the input force is less than the weight of the ball. Other levers are used to magnify the distance that the load (the ball, in this case) moves. Which type of lever did you build, one that magnifies force or one that magnifies distance?

Teacher Information   Perfect Pitcher

The students design pitching arms for distance and accuracy.

This ball thrower is a first-class lever. The motor is used to pull the arm back in preparation for launching.

Objectives
1. To design a robotic arm for throwing.
2. To write a program in which a motor is activated by a touch sensor.
3. To identify types of levers and part of levers.

Materials
NXT
Computer
Motors
Touch sensor

LEGO® pieces
Rubber bands
String
Plastic ball
Plate and cup for target
Meter sticks
Tape

Time: Approximately 90 minutes

Notes

1. For the distance contest, mark the starting line with tape and position meter sticks along the course so that the distances can be measured easily. You may want to use tape or stickers to mark where the balls land.

2. For the accuracy contest, tape or glue a cup to the center of a plate to make the target. For scoring, award three points if the ball lands in the central cup (even if it then bounces out). Award two points if it touches the inner cup without going inside. Award one point if the ball hits the plate but not the inner cup.

3. As written, this activity has the students identify classes of levers. If you wish to de-emphasize levers, this activity can be done with only the first page of the student handout, omitting the questions about levers.

4. As an introduction, you may want to show the students pictures of catapults (third-class levers) and trebuchets (first-class levers) and discuss how they work.

5. Allow the students to practice in the distance and accuracy areas as much as they wish before the contest begins, adjusting their machines as needed.

6. This activity is a good one for encouraging the students to make methodical changes and note their effects. For example, they can vary the length of time the motors are turned on, the position of the fulcrum, or the length of the throwing arm.

Answers to Perfect Pitcher

1. Answers will vary.
2. Answers will vary.
3. Answers will vary.
4. Answers will vary. One common problem is that the students try to increase the accuracy or throwing distance of the arm by lengthening it, to the point of not having enough torque to lift it.
5. Answers will vary. The trebuchet is a first-class lever, with the fulcrum in the middle. The catapult is a third-class lever with the fulcrum at one end, the effort force close to the fulcrum, and the load at the far end of the lever arm.
6. Whether the students build a first-class lever or a third-class lever, it will almost certainly magnify the distance rather than the force.

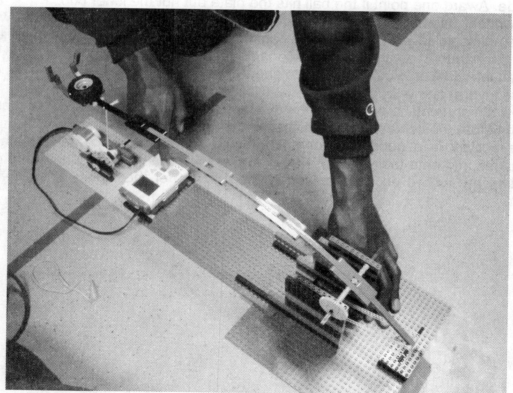

This pitching arm is able to throw the ball more than four meters.

Pulley Systems

Different pulley systems have different ideal mechanical advantages, depending upon their configurations. Can you construct a pulley system (using as many or as few pulleys as you wish) with an ideal mechanical advantage of one? Of two? Of six?

Construct a pulley system for each of the following ideal mechanical advantages. Once your pulley system is complete, make a sketch of it, then have the teacher check it to make sure it is correct.

I.M.A.	Sketch of pulley system	Teacher check
1		
2		
3		

4		
5		
6		

Teacher Information   Pulley Systems

This activity allows the students to explore pulley systems and to calculate the mechanical advantage for different systems.

1. To rig pulley systems.
2. To find the ideal mechanical advantage of various systems.

Materials
LEGO® pieces, including pulleys
String
Weighted brick or mass to be lifted

Time: Approximately 40 minutes

Notes
1. The students should have some understanding of mechanical advantage before beginning the activity.
2. Encourage the students to begin by building a frame to support the pulleys. Doing so will making rigging the more complicated systems easier.
3. If you wish, you can award points or prizes at the end based upon the number of pulley systems completed correctly.

Answers to Pulley Systems

1. Single fixed pulley
Ideal mechanical advantage of one

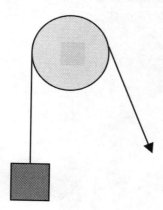

2. One fixed pulley, one movable pulley
Ideal mechanical advantage of two

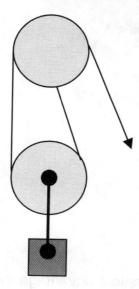

3. One fixed pulley, one movable pulley
Ideal mechanical advantage of three

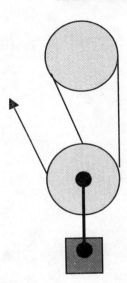

4. Two fixed pulleys, two movable pulleys
Ideal mechanical advantage of four

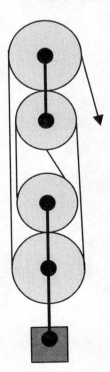

5. Two fixed pulleys, two movable pulleys
Ideal mechanical advantage of five

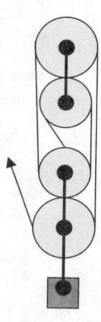

6. Three fixed pulleys, three movable pulleys
Ideal mechanical advantage of six

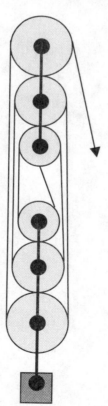

Ramp Up

Design and build a car that can climb as steep a ramp as possible. Run your car with both motors on full power.

1. Test your car. How steep a ramp can your car climb? Record the angle in degrees.

2. Describe a problem your car encountered. (For example, it veered to the left or the wheels slid instead of rolling.)

3. Describe a change you could make to your car. Explain the physics behind your idea—why you think the change will improve your car's performance.

4. Make the change and test your car again. Did the change help?

5. How steep a ramp can your car climb this time? Record the angle in degrees.

6. Describe a problem your car encountered in this trial.

7. Describe another change you could make to your car. Explain the physics behind your idea.

8. Make the change and test your car again. Did this change help?

9. How steep a ramp can your car climb this time? Record the angle in degrees.

10. Make a sketch of your most successful car.

11. What is the steepest angle that your car was able to climb?

Teacher Information

Ramp Up

This activity gives the students practical experience with a number of concepts in physics, including friction, torque, and center of gravity. It also pushes them to make use of the engineering design process—design, build, test, redesign and retest.

An NXT car climbs the ramp. An eight-tooth gear meshed with a forty-tooth gear is used on each motor to gear down the car and increase the torque.

Objectives
1. To build a ramp-climbing car.
2. To be able to analyze the car's performance in terms of physical concepts.
3. To make use of the engineering design process.

Materials
NXT
Computer
Motors
LEGO® pieces, including wheels
Adjustable ramp
Protractor for measuring angles

Time: Approximately 90 minutes

Notes

1. To construct the ramp, you will need a sturdy board approximately one meter long. To make the angle adjustable, you can support the top of the board on a bookshelf, moving the top from shelf to shelf to adjust the angle. Another possibility is to support the top of the board with a ring stand and clamps.

2. If the students reach a dead end in trying to improve the vehicle, help them to analyze the problems they are encountering. If the wheels slip, they may want to try a different type of tires. If the car stalls in one place, they may want to gear it down to increase torque. If the car tips backward, they may want to lower its center of gravity.

3. Torque enters into many aspects of this lab. First, the students can increase the torque of their motors by gearing down the cars. Second, increasing the wheel size decreases the force with which the wheel pushes against the ground, since the torque of the motor is more-or-less constant and the distance to the point where the force is applied increases with the radius of the wheel. Third, the cars tend to veer sideways as the ramp gets steeper. Mounting the forward wheel(s) well in front of the NXT will tend to counteract this tendency by producing a counter-torque.

4. The handout requires the students to make two design modifications and test them. If time permits, the students may continue to refine their designs.

5. The students can use trigonometry to calculate the angle more precisely using the height and length of the ramp. An example of a spreadsheet program for performing this calculation is shown below. The program was designed by Andrew Hart, a design and technology teacher at John Calvin Christian College, Armadale, Western Australia.

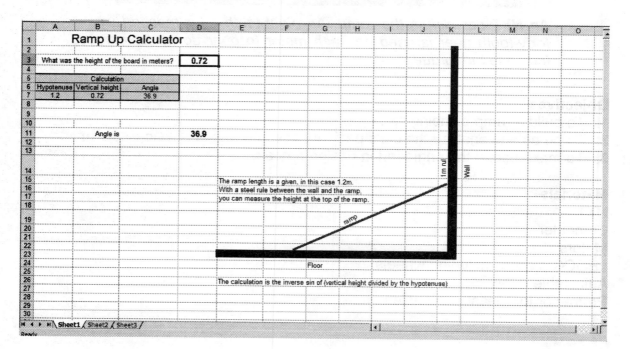

Peak Performance

Challenge: You are going on a difficult journey across a valley and up a steep mountain. Build a car to take you there. Your car must climb as steep a mountain as possible. In addition, it must cross the valley quickly.

Scoring: Your car's score will be calculated by taking the steepest angle your car climbs successfully on the ramp (the mountain) and subtracting the time it takes to cross the floor (the valley). For example, suppose your car crosses the floor in 5 seconds and climbs a 45-degree ramp. Your score would be 45 - 5 = 40.

Good luck!

1. Angle of ramp climbed:

2. Time to cross valley:

3. Final score (angle minus time):

Often, engineers find that two of their goals conflict with one another. For example, making an airplane stronger may increase its weight, making takeoff more difficult. The engineers must make trade-offs, compromising on individual goals to make the overall product work better.

4. Describe a trade-off you faced in this activity. How did you solve the conflict?

Teacher Information   Peak Performance

This activity builds upon what the students learned in Ramp Up, adding an additional design goal (speed on level ground) and having them grapple with conflicting design goals (speed and ramp-climbing ability) to find a good overall solution.

A car climbs a ramp. The weighted brick at the front helps to prevent the car from tipping backwards.

Objectives
1. To determine the attributes necessary for a good ramp-climbing car.
2. To determine the attributes necessary for a speedy car.
3. To balance trade-offs when two design goals conflict.

Materials
NXT
Computer
Motors
LEGO® pieces, including wheels
Adjustable ramp
Protractor for measuring angles
Meter stick
Tape for marking "valley"

Time: Approximately 60 minutes

Notes

1. You may want to set a minimum score which students must achieve. Using a wooden ramp with a fairly rough surface and a 1.5-meter-long valley, all of the cars should be able to achieve a score of at least 35. The best cars will probably have scores above 50.
2. This activity uses the same ramp as the previous one, Ramp Up.
3. If this activity is conducted without doing Ramp Up first, allow at least 90 minutes to complete it.
4. If the students reach a dead end in trying to improve the vehicle, help them to analyze the problems they are encountering. If the wheels slip, they may want to try a different type of tires. If the car stalls in one place, they may want to gear it down to increase torque. If the car tips backward, they may want to lower its center of gravity.
5. Torque enters into many aspects of this lab. First, the students can increase the torque of their motors by gearing down the cars. Second, increasing the wheel size decreases the force with which the wheel pushes against the ground, since the torque of the motor is more-or-less constant and the distance to the point where the force is applied increases with the radius of the wheel. Third, the cars tend to veer sideways as the ramp gets steeper. Mounting the forward wheel(s) well in front of the NXT will tend to counteract this tendency by producing a counter-torque.
6. The students can use trigonometry to calculate the angle more precisely using the height and length of the ramp. An example of a spreadsheet program for performing this calculation is shown below. The program was designed by Andrew Hart, a design and technology teacher at John Calvin Christian College, Armadale, Western Australia.

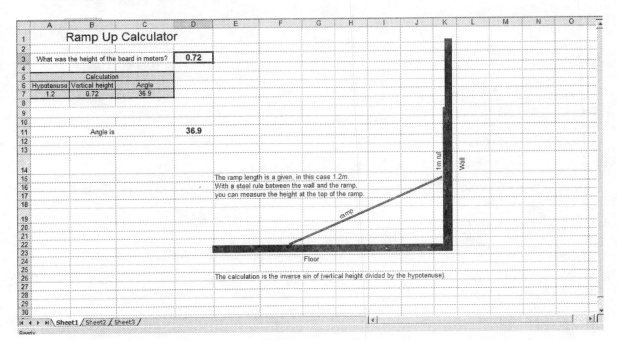

Answers to Peak Performance

1. **Angle of ramp climbed:** Answers will vary, depending upon the surface of the ramp, types of tires available, etc. Using a wooden board, most cars should be able to climb an angle of between 40 and 55 degrees.
2. **Time to cross valley:** Answers will vary. Most cars should take under five seconds.
3. **Final score (angle minus time):** Answers will vary. For a 1.5-meter-long "valley," a score above thirty-five is reasonable; a score above fifty is excellent.
4. **Many students will describe the trade-off they faced between torque and speed. In order to climb a steep ramp, they needed to increase the torque by gearing down. However, gearing down slowed down the car, increasing the time it took to cross the valley. The students needed to decide upon a compromise between these two conflicting goals. Another trade-off that students wrestle with is wheel size. Large wheels make the car go faster. However, they also reduce the force with which the wheels push against the ramp, hurting the car's performance on the ramp.**

Balancing Nails

It is quite easy to balance a single LEGO® nail on a stand. Can you find a way to balance more?

Part I: Balancing Act

Balance as many nails as you can.

1. How many nails were you able to balance?

2. Make a sketch of your arrangement below.

Part II: Long and Short

Once you know the trick for balancing eight nails, try balancing two different lengths of nails. First use twelve-stud-axle nails. To balance the nails, first arrange them on the ground, then lift them as a group and place them on the stand.

Once you are successful at balancing the long nails, replace the six side nails with six-stud-axle nails and try again.

1. Was it harder to balance the long nails or the short nails?

2. Explain your results in terms of center of gravity.

Teacher Information   Balancing Nails

The students balance LEGO® nails.

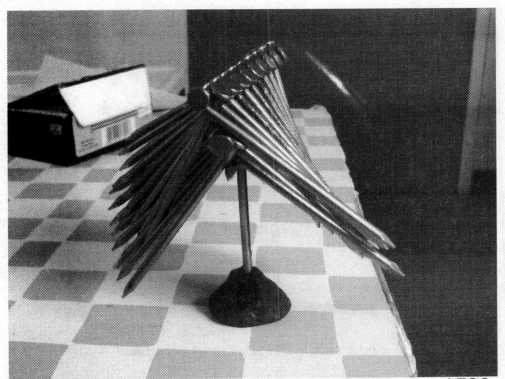

The balancing act can be done with actual nails as well as LEGO nails. Here, forty nails are balanced on a single nail.

Objectives
1. To apply concepts of center of gravity and stability to balance nails.
2. To investigate how shifting the center of gravity upward affects stability.

Materials
LEGO pieces
Nails (optional)
Wooden block or clay (optional)

Time: Approximately 40 minutes

Notes
1. Give the students the two parts of this lab separately, because the second part gives away the answer to the first part. Before beginning the second part, demonstrate how to balance eight nails, if the students did not figure it out for themselves.

2. To make the long nails, attach a round plate and a skid plate to the top of a twelve-stud axle. For the short nails used in Part II, use six-stud axles. To make the stand, mount a twelve-stud axle vertically. Place a bushing on the top. (See the photograph below.)

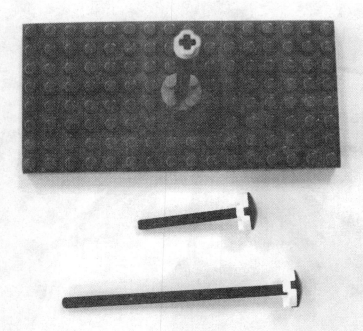

The stand, a short nail, and a long nail.

3. To balance the nails, first arrange them on the ground, then lift them as a group and place them on the stand. (See the photograph below.)

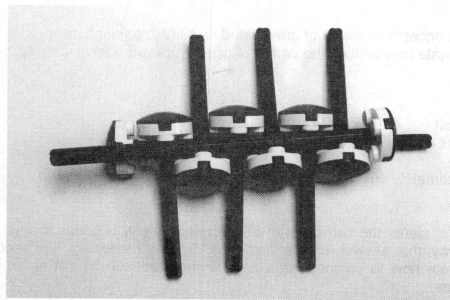

Short nails arranged on the ground, ready to be lifted onto the stand.

4. Before starting this project, make sure that the students have an understanding of center of gravity and stability. In particular, the students should understand that an object is at stable equilibrium if its center of gravity is below its balance point. They should also realize that the center of gravity of an object does not have to part of the object.
5. Part I of this activity can also be done with real nails.

Answers to Balancing Nails

Part I: Balancing Act
1. **Answers will vary.**
2. **Answers will vary. The photograph below shows an arrangement for balancing eight nails.**

Part II: Long and Short
1. **The longer nails are easier to balance.**
2. **The arrangement of the longer nails has a lower center of gravity. Because its center of gravity is below the balancing point, this arrangement is stable.**

Acknowledgement: This activity is based upon an activity at the Museum of Science, Boston.

Tightrope Walker

Walking on a tightrope isn't always as difficult as it looks. Often, the performers find ways to lower their center of gravity in order to make balancing easier. In fact, if the walker's center of gravity is below the rope, he or she will tend to return to an upright position if disturbed.

Build your own LEGO® tightrope walker, at least ten centimeters tall. The walker will be mounted on a pulley. The pulley will roll along a string stretched taut and anchored at the ends. Both the pulley and the walker must remain above the rope. However, the walker can have arms, legs, or accessories that dangle below the rope. He or she can even be holding onto a person or animal that dangles below the rope.

1. Make a sketch of your walker below.

2. Place an X at its approximate center of gravity.

Teacher Information   Tightrope Walker

The students build tightrope walkers out of LEGO® pieces.

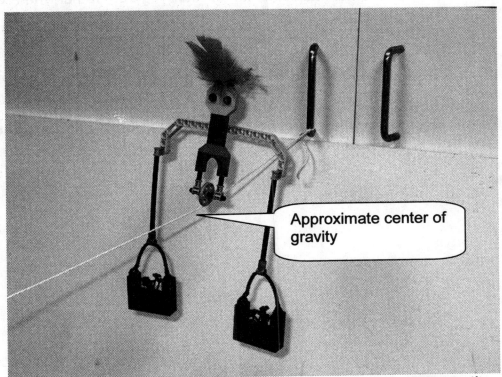

The weighted bricks that form the flower baskets help to lower the figure's center of gravity.

Objectives
1. To apply concepts of center of gravity and stability to build a LEGO tightrope walker.
2. To use the engineering design process.

Materials
LEGO pieces
String
Craft materials

Time: Approximately 40 minutes

Notes
1. Before starting this project, make sure that the students have an understanding of center of gravity and stability. In particular, the students should understand that an object is at stable equilibrium if its center of gravity is below its balance point. They should also realize that the center of gravity of an object does not have to

be on a physical part of the actual object. For example, the center of gravity of a hoop is at the center of the hoop.

2. Getting the tightrope walkers to balance will probably require several rounds of adjustment after the completed figures are placed on the tightrope. Encourage the students to make small adjustments to their figures rather than wholesale changes.

Answers to Tightrope Walker

1. Answers will vary.
2. If the object is stable, the center of gravity should lie directly underneath the figure, below the tightrope.

LEGO® Balance

Build your own pan balance out of LEGO® pieces, string, and a set of standard metric masses.

Here are your design specifications:

•Your balance must be able to mass objects between 0 and 50 grams.

•Your balance must be able to measure to within 0.5 grams of the actual mass of the object. (You're welcome to make it more precise, of course.)

Other than these two constraints, the design is up to you. After you have built your balance, you may test it (and make improvements to it) as many times as you wish. A regular balance is available so that you can compare the results from it with those from your LEGO balance.

When you are confident that your balance can measure to within 0.5 grams of the actual mass, you are ready for the official test. You will be given a basket containing four objects, labeled 1, 2, 3, and 4, and asked to find the mass of each one.

Good luck!

Balance Test

You will be given a basket containing four objects, labeled 1, 2, 3, and 4. Mass each object and write down the answer below.

Object Number	Mass in grams
1	
2	
3	
4	

Teacher Information

LEGO® Balance

The students build LEGO® balances that are accurate to within 0.5 grams.

The weighted bricks on the arms of this balance help it to be self-leveling by lowering the center of gravity below the place where the arms are attached to the base.

Objectives
1. To apply concepts of center of gravity and torque to build a LEGO balance.
2. To gain comfort using the metric system.
3. To use the engineering design process.

Materials
LEGO pieces
Set of metric masses
String
Pan balance
Electronic or triple-beam balance
Objects for massing

Time: Approximately 180 minutes

Notes
1. At first, this project can seem daunting to students, since they are being asked to construct a precise and accurate balance out of LEGO pieces. However, the nature of the task also gives them a real sense of accomplishment when they

complete it successfully. The way in which the activity is structured virtually guarantees their success.

2. Make sure that the students are familiar with pan balances before starting this project. Let them use a pan balance to mass a few objects to get a solid sense of how the balance works. It is also helpful to have different types of pan balances, or pictures of them, so that students may see some of the various ways of attaching the pans to the arm.

3. Designing a balance requires an understanding of torque (or levers), since an object further out along an arm of the balance will exert a greater torque than one close to the pivot point. The students can make use of this concept to increase the precision of the balance by making the arms longer.

4. A common design flaw in the students' balances is to have the center of gravity above the balance point. In this case, the arms tend to swing wildly if disturbed, rather than coming to rest in a horizontal position. Adding a pair of weighted bricks to the underside of the arms will lower the center of gravity and improve the performance of the balance. If a group of students is experiencing the problem of an unstable balance, try turning their balance upside down. Then, the center of gravity is below the balance point, the moving part of the balance is at stable equilibrium, and the balance behaves much better. You can leave the students to figure out why turning the balance upside down helped. Ask them questions to get them thinking along the right lines if necessary.

5. Another common design flaw is to anchor the pans to the arms at more than one point. If the students do this, their balance will behave like a seesaw, with objects placed at the outer edge of the pan appearing to have more mass than those placed on the inner edge.

6. In general, the easiest design to make work is one with high arms and pans suspended by strings.

7. The assessment for this activity shifts much of the responsibility to the students, since they are deciding when their balance is ready to be tested. Before giving them the bag of unknown objects to test, make sure that they have tested their balance on a number of practice objects, covering the full range of masses between zero grams and fifty grams.

8. When the students bring their completed test to you, you may want to scan it before grading it to make sure that their answers are in the right ballpark. On a few occasions, I have had a group submit a test with inaccurate answers. I hand the test back to them without grading it and look at their balance with them to try to pinpoint the problems. After they have modified the balance and conducted more trials, I give them a different basket of unknowns for their test.

Building Pressure

Make a stack of eight two-stud-by-four-stud LEGO® bricks. Set the stack on a table. The stack of bricks is exerting pressure on the table—the weight of the eight bricks pushing down on the area of the table covered by one brick, or a ratio of 8:1.

1. Using all eight LEGO bricks, rearrange them so that they are exerting only half as much pressure on the table as the original stack (in other words, you want your new grouping to have a ratio of 4:1). Sketch your arrangement.

2. Split your eight bricks into two groups of four. Arrange each group so that it exerts a different amount of pressure on the table than the other group of four does. Sketch your arrangement.

3. Next, split the eight bricks into two groups of unequal size, but arrange each group so that it exerts the same pressure on the table. Sketch your arrangement.

4. Arrange the eight bricks so that they exert as low a pressure on the table as possible. Sketch your arrangement.

5. Arrange the eight bricks so that they exert as high a pressure on the table as possible. (The bottom of the stack must rest flat against the table.) Sketch your arrangement.

Teacher Information

Building Pressure

This activity gives the students a chance to experiment with the concept of pressure.

One method of exerting as much pressure as possible on the table with eight LEGO® bricks. A variety of solutions are possible.

Objectives
1. To gain an understanding of the concept of pressure.
2. To find creative solutions to problems.

Materials
2 x 4 LEGO bricks

Time: Approximately 30 minutes

Notes
1. Give the students LEGO bricks to manipulate as they work on the activity. Each student or group of students will need eight bricks.
2. If you wish, you may have the students mass the bricks and measure their dimensions, so that they will be able to calculate the pressure in standard units, rather than using ratios.

Answers to Building Pressure

1. One possibility is to place two stacks of four bricks each side by side.

2. There are many possible answers. One is to form one group of four bricks into a single stack and the second group into two stacks of two. The tall stack has a brick/area ratio of 4:1. The other group has a ratio of 2:1.

3. Again, there are many possibilities. For example one group could be made up of a single stack of bricks two high, while the other group could contain three stacks of two bricks. Both groups have a ratio of 2:1.

4. Spread the bricks out in a single layer, with a ratio of 1:1.

5. Place one brick on its end and attach the other seven to it. Since the end of the brick has about one-third the area of the bottom of the brick, this arrangement has a brick/area ratio of roughly 21:1.

Allowing the bricks to hang over the edge of the table leads to even better solutions.

Floating LEGO® Bricks

How dense is a LEGO® weighted brick? To find out, you will first need to find the mass and volume of the brick.

1. Use a balance to find the mass of the weighted brick. Record your answer in grams.

2. Find the volume of the brick, either by displacement or by measuring the length, width, and height and multiplying them together. Record your answer in cubic centimeters.

3. Find the density of the brick by dividing the mass by the volume. Record your answer.

Now, your challenge is to make your weighted brick float by adding pairs of two-stud-by-six-stud unweighted bricks to the top of it.

4. These pairs of bricks are the same volume as the weighted brick, though not the same mass. Use the balance to find the mass of a pair of bricks. Next, find the density of the pair. Record your answers.

5. Before you try adding any pairs of bricks to your weighted brick, calculate how many pairs you will need. (Remember, the density of water is 1.0 g/cm^3.) Show your calculations below.

6. Once you have calculated how many bricks you will need, build your stack and try floating it. Did it float?

7. Answer 7a if your stack floated and 7b if it did not.
   a. If your stack floated, remove a pair of bricks and try again. If the new stack still floats, calculate its density. Show your work.

   b. If your stack did not float, add pairs of bricks until the stack floats. Find the density of the new stack. Show your work.

Teacher Information   Floating LEGO® Bricks

The students find the density of a weighted brick, and then calculate how many unweighted bricks must be placed on top of it in order for the entire stack to float.

A weighted brick, topped by twelve unweighted bricks, floats.

Objectives
1. To use a balance to find mass.
2. To find volume, either by displacement or by measuring the dimensions of the object.
3. To find the density of an object.
4. To understand how density and buoyancy are related.
5. To use density to solve a problem.

Materials
Balance, preferably precise to at least hundredths of a gram
Weighted brick
Metric ruler
Container for measuring volume by displacement (optional)
2 x 8 LEGO bricks
Container at least 15 cm tall for floating stack

Time: Approximately 40 minutes

Notes
1. The students should be taught to use the balances before beginning this lab.
2. The students should be familiar with the concepts of mass, volume, and density before beginning this activity.
3. In creating the stack, the weighted brick must be at the bottom of the stack, so that air is trapped inside the unweighted bricks.
4. The floating stack is approximately 14 cm high.

Answers to Floating LEGO® Bricks

1. The mass of a weighted brick is generally somewhere between 52.9 grams and 53.5 grams.
2. The dimensions of the weighted brick are approximately 4.8 cm by 1.5 cm by 1.9 cm. Its volume is around 14 cm^3.
3. Assuming a mass of 53 grams and a volume of 14 cm^3, the density of the weighted brick is around 3.8 g/cm^3.
4. The mass of a pair of 2 x 8 bricks is around 7.0 grams. The volume is the same as that of the weighted brick, around 14 cm^3. The density of the pair is approximately 0.5 g/cm^3.
5. To make the stack float, its density must be less than 1.0 g/cm^3. If you add six pairs of 2 x 8 bricks to the weighted brick, the total mass of the stack will be approximately 42 + 53 = 95 grams. The total volume of the stack will be approximately 7 x 14 = 98 grams. With a density of 0.97 g/cm^3, this stack should float. Depending upon the mass of the weighted brick used, the number of 2 x 8 bricks needed may vary slightly.
6. Answers will vary.
7. Answers will vary.

Cartesian Diver

A Cartesian diver is an object that floats in a sealed bottle until the bottle is squeezed, at which point the object sinks. When the pressure on the bottle is released, the object rises back to the top. Make a Cartesian diver out of an eyedropper.

1. What changes do you see inside the dropper as it goes up and down?

Now you are ready to design your own diver. Make a diver that is able to go up and down, using the materials provided.

2. Sketch your successful diver below, labeling the materials used.

Use what you have learned to make a LEGO® diver—a minifigure that goes up and down. You may use other LEGO pieces and/or the other materials provided.

3. Sketch your diver, labeling the materials used.

4. Based upon your experimentation, what properties must an object have in order to be a Cartesian diver?

Teacher Information

Cartesian Diver

This activity gives the students a chance to experiment with the concepts of buoyancy, density, and pressure.

Two students squeeze their bottles to make LEGO® minifigures sink to the bottom. The figure on the right has a marshmallow on its head.

Objectives
1. To gain an understanding of the concepts of buoyancy, density, and pressure.
2. To find creative solutions to problems.

Materials
One-liter plastic soda bottle with lid
Glass eyedropper with rubber bulb
LEGO minifigures
Materials for making Cartesian divers (see below)

Time: Approximately 60 minutes

Notes

1. A Cartesian diver is an object that barely floats in a sealed bottle. When the bottle is squeezed, the object sinks. When the pressure on the bottle is released, the object rises back to the top.

2. A variety of compressible materials can be used to create Cartesian divers. Cranberries, pieces of mushroom, and small marshmallows (though they disintegrate over time) are foods that work well. Non-food possibilities include Styrofoam, cork, and uninflated balloons. In addition, you will need heavier materials to provide weight, such as paper clips, pipe cleaners, and metal washers.

3. To turn the eyedropper into a Cartesian diver, fill it partly full of water so that it barely floats. As they squeeze the bottle, the students will be able to see the water level rise in the dropper.

4. To turn the other materials into Cartesian divers, combine a compressible material, such as a small marshmallow, with enough added weight so that the combination barely floats.

5. To turn a minifigure into a Cartesian diver, it may be necessary to add a floating compressible material and/or a weight. Some minifigures, such as the ghost, will trap enough air that they do not need any added compressible material. Some minifigures will be dense enough that they need little or no added weight.

6. Depending upon the size of the bottle opening, you may need to raise the minifigure's arms over its head in order to fit the figure into the bottle.

Answers to Cartesian Diver

1. The water level rises inside the dropper as it goes to the bottom of the bottle and drops as the dropper returns to the surface.
2. Answers will vary.
3. Answers will vary.
4. To be a Cartesian diver, an object needs to include a compressible material. It also needs to barely float.

Stir It Up

People stir hot drinks to cool them down. Does stirring really help? Find out, using an NXT, a motorized stirrer, and a temperature sensor.

Build a LEGO® stirrer. To construct it, attach a long axle to a motor. Next, design a part that can be attached to the axle to stir the water when the motor is turned on.

For the stirring program, log the temperature sensor in degrees Celsius once every five seconds for 500 seconds. Run the stirrer motor at full power.

Use LEGO pieces to build a holder for the temperature sensor. The holder should fit over the rim of the cup, positioning the temperature sensor so that most of the metal tip is in the water while the rest of the sensor is above it. Attach the holder and stirrer to the cup. Test your set-up by running the program briefly. Now, add hot liquid.

Run the test and upload the data to the computer. Run the test a second time, making sure that you use the same amount and temperature of water, but do not turn the stirrer on. Upload the data.

1. Why is it important to run the test twice, once with the stirrer on and once with it off?

2. Based upon your results, does stirring cool the liquid down faster?

Teacher Information   Stir It Up

In this activity, the students build LEGO® stirrers and use them to test whether stirring a hot drink speeds cooling.

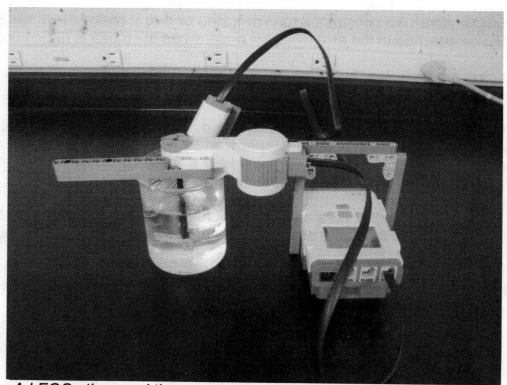

A LEGO stirrer and thermometer are used to test 200 ml of hot water in a beaker.

Objectives
1. To use a computer to collect, graph, and analyze data.
2. To understand the importance of having a control when running an experiment.
3. To understand how heat energy can be dissipated.

Materials
NXT
Computer
Temperature sensor
Motor
LEGO parts
Beaker or mug
Hot water

Time: Approximately 40 minutes

Notes

1. This activity and the next two are related. The students use what they learn in the first two activities to design and build a cooling device in the third.

2. This activity is similar in many ways to the next one, It's a Breeze. The students can do both to gain practice in logging and analyzing data. Alternatively, half the class can do Stir It Up while the other half does It's a Breeze. The groups can then share their results and all of the students can apply what they've learned in Cool It Fast.

3. Most students will be surprised to discover that stirring does not help to cool the hot liquid. This activity contrasts nicely with It's a Breeze, where students discover that blowing on hot liquid does help to cool it.

4. Make sure that the students understand the importance of a control in their experiment. All of the conditions for the stirrer and control containers should be the same except for the stirrer—same amount of water, same initial temperature, etc. If two temperature sensors per group are available, the experimental and control set-ups can be run simultaneously. Otherwise, they can be run serially.

5. This activity can be used to discuss heat transfer. Heat is transferred to the cup and to the boundary layer of air adjacent to the liquid by conduction. The warmer air then rises, carrying heat away with it (convection). Does stirring help speed this process? Not in this case. Stirring increases the movement of liquid within the cup, but the temperature within a small cup is already relatively uniform. Thus, bringing liquid from the center of the cup to the surface does not enhance the cooling. (If you were doing this experiment using a large vat of hot liquid, then stirring would help, because the temperature of the liquid would not be uniform throughout the vat and stirring would help to mix it.)

6. Be sure to keep the liquid away from the motors, the cables, and the NXT.

7. A stable, heat-resistant container, such as a 250-ml glass beaker or coffee mug, works best for this experiment.

Sample Program for Stir It Up

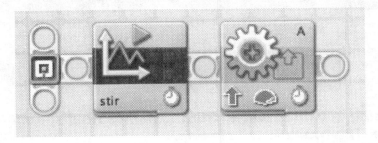

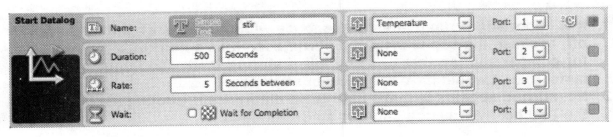

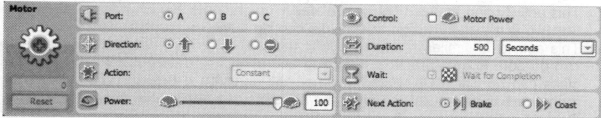

This sample program logs the temperature sensor for 500 seconds, recording a data point once every five seconds while running the motorized stirrer. Run it once to collect the experimental data and a second time to collect the control data.

Answers to Stir It Up

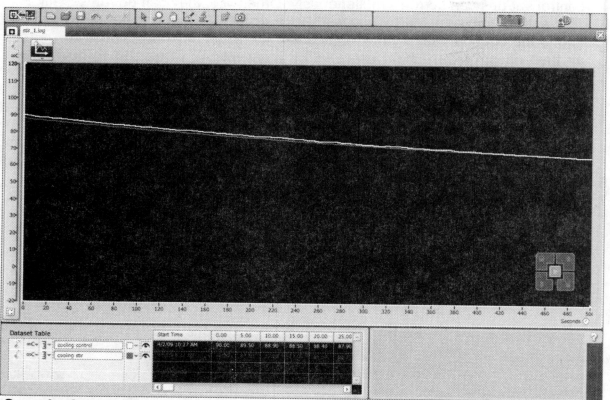

Sample data using 200 ml of water: Stirring makes no discernible difference in the cooling rate. The two curves coincide.

1. It is important to run the test twice, once with the stirrer on and once with it off, because the cup without the stirrer serves as a control. It gives a basis for comparison, so that one can tell if stirring made the temperature drop faster than it would have in an undisturbed cup.
2. No, stirring appears to make little or no difference in cooling the liquid. (See the Teacher Information page for an explanation.)

It's a Breeze

People blow on hot drinks to cool them down. Does blowing really help? Find out, using an NXT, a temperature sensor, and a fan.

For the program, log the temperature sensor in degrees Celsius once every five seconds for 500 seconds.

Use a portable fan to create the breeze for this activity. Position the fan and the cup so that the breeze blows across the surface of the hot liquid.

Use LEGO® pieces to build a holder for the temperature sensor. The holder should fit over the rim of the cup, positioning the temperature sensor so that most of the metal tip is in the water while the rest of the sensor is above it. Attach the holder to the cup and add hot liquid to the cup.

Run the test and upload the data to the computer. Run the test a second time, making sure that you use the same amount and temperature of water, but do not turn the fan on. Upload the data.

1. Why is it important to run the test twice, once with the fan on and once with it off?

2. Based upon your results, does blowing cool the liquid down faster?

Teacher Information

It's a Breeze

In this activity, the students use a portable fan to test whether or not blowing on a hot drink speeds cooling.

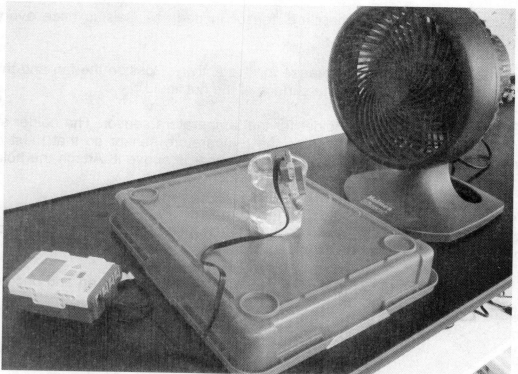

A portable fan blows across the cup of hot liquid as it cools.

Objectives
1. To use a computer to collect, graph, and analyze data.
2. To understand the importance of having a control when running an experiment.
3. To understand how heat energy can be dissipated.

Materials
NXT
Computer
Temperature sensor
LEGO® pieces
Portable fan
Beaker or mug
Hot water

Time: Approximately 30 minutes

Notes

1. This activity is the second of three related experiments. The students use what they learn in the first two to design and build a cooling device in the third.

2. This activity is similar in many ways to the previous one, Stir It up. The students can do both to gain practice in logging and analyzing data. Alternatively, half the class can do Stir It Up while the other half does It's a Breeze. The groups can then share their results and all of the students can apply what they've learned in Cool It Fast.

3. The students will discover that blowing does help to cool the hot liquid. This activity contrasts nicely with Stir It Up, where the students discover that stirring a hot liquid does not help to cool it.

4. Make sure that the students understand the importance of a control in their experiment. All of the conditions for the experimental and control containers should be the same except for the fan—same amount of water, same initial temperature, etc. If two temperature sensors per group are available, the actual and control experiments can be run simultaneously. Otherwise, they can be run serially.

5. This activity can be used to discuss heat transfer by convection. In convection, heat is transferred by the movement of a heated substance itself, such as the blowing of heated air. When a cup of hot liquid cools, convection currents carry the heated air upward, since the heated air is less dense. The air currents produced by the fan accelerate this process, carrying the heated air away at a much faster pace, allowing cooler air to take its place and be heated by the liquid.

6. Be sure to keep the liquid away from the motors, the cables, and the NXT.

7. This activity works well with a 250-ml beaker or standard-sized coffee cup filled almost to the brim.

Sample Program for It's a Breeze

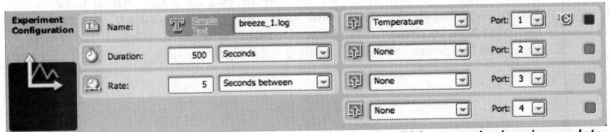

This sample program logs the temperature sensor for 500 seconds, logging a data point once every five seconds. Run it once to collect the experimental data and a second time to collect the control data. If two temperature sensors per group are available, both sets of data can be collected simultaneously.

Answers to It's a Breeze

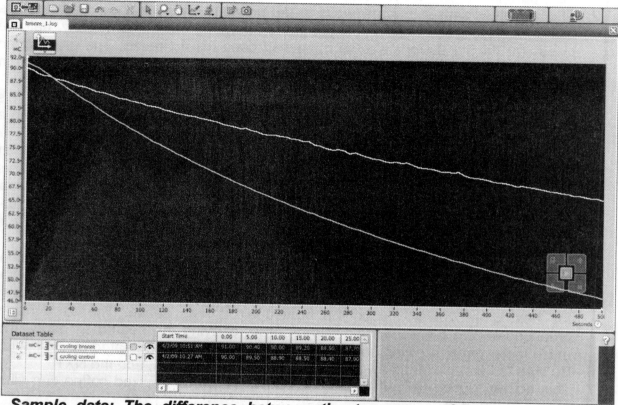

Sample data: The difference between the top curve, the control, and the bottom curve, cooled with a fan, shows that the fan increases the rate of cooling.

1. It is important to run the test twice, once with the fan on and once with it off, because the test without the fan serves as a control. It gives a basis for comparison, so that one can tell if the moving air caused the temperature to drop faster than it would have in an undisturbed cup.
2. Yes, the fan increases the cooling rate significantly.

Cool It Fast

You are impatient to drink your cocoa, but it is too hot. You do not want to wait for it to cool. Build and program a device that will speed up its cooling.

Build a stirrer, a fan, or your own idea for a cooling device.

Write a program to run your device while collecting temperature data every five seconds for 500 seconds.

Set up your device to cool a cup of hot liquid. Remember to position the temperature sensor inside the cup so that the metal tip will be submerged, but the rest of the sensor will not.

Run your program and upload the data. Refill the cup with hot liquid and run the experiment again with your device turned off. Upload the data and compare the two data sets.

1. Sketch your device and write a brief description of it.

2. Did your device cool the liquid more quickly than in the control cup?

3. If you had more time, how would you improve your device?

Teacher Information

Cool It Fast

In this activity, the students build and test their own devices to speed the cooling of a hot drink.

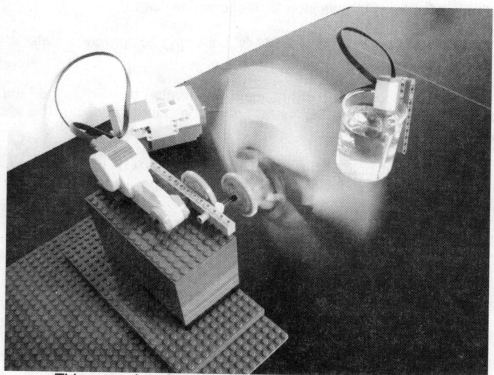

This geared-up fan has blades made of thin cardboard.

Objectives
1. To use a computer to collect, graph, and analyze data.
2. To understand the importance of having a control, or other meaningful basis for comparison, when running an experiment.
3. To understand how heat energy can be dissipated.
4. To make use of what has been learned to design a cooling device.

Materials
NXT
Computer
Temperature sensor
Motor
LEGO® parts
Beaker or mug
Hot water

Time: Approximately 60 minutes

Notes
1. This activity is the third of three related experiments. The students use what they learned in the first two to design and build a cooling device in the third.
2. This activity can be used to assess the students' understanding of heat transfer, because they are using what they have learned to design an effective cooling device. Based upon the previous labs, most students will probably choose to build fans.
3. Make sure that the students understand the importance of a control in the design of their experiment. All of the conditions for the experimental and control set-ups should be the same except for the cooling device—same amount of water, same initial temperature, etc. If you wish, you can run one control for the entire class, as long as everyone agrees upon the initial conditions.
4. If the students wish to compare their devices with each other, make sure that they understand the importance of keeping all of the other factors the same. If the initial conditions differ, then the comparison is meaningless.
5. Be sure to keep the liquid away from the motors, the cables, and the NXT.

Hearing Test

Ideally, the human ear can detect frequencies between about 20 and 20,000 hertz. However, as people get older, they lose the ability to hear higher frequencies. Use the NXT to measure the hearing range of several people of varying ages.

Download the hearing-test program to the NXT. When you run the program, it will display a frequency on the screen and play the corresponding tone, starting with 2000 Hz. When the touch sensor is pressed, the next frequency will be displayed and played. The frequency is increased by 1000 Hz each time.

The internal speakers of the NXT can play tones up to a frequency of around 11,500 Hz. Past that point, the tone does not change. So, stop each test when you reach 12,000 Hz.

1. Test three people. Note the highest tone each one was able to hear, plus his or her approximate age.

   First test:
   Approximate age of person_____

   Highest frequency detected_____

   Second test:
   Approximate age of person_____

   Highest frequency detected_____

   Third test:
   Approximate age of person_____

   Highest frequency detected_____

2. Did you find anyone who was not able to hear the highest tones? If so, approximately how old was the person?

3. Examine the class data. Did there appear to be a correlation between age and ability to hear high frequencies?

Teacher Information

Hearing Test

In this activity, the students use the NXT to test people's abilities to hear high frequencies.

Objectives
1. To use the NXT to investigate the ability to hear different frequencies.
2. To see if the ability to hear high frequencies declines with age.

Materials
NXT
Computer
Touch sensor

Time: Approximately 30 minutes

Notes
1. The program required for this activity is fairly sophisticated. Unless you wish the students to gain additional programming practice, you can write the program ahead of time and have the students download it to their computers or give them the sample program sheet to copy.
2. The tones played by the NXT's internal speakers are approximately correct for the range used in this activity, though they become less accurate above 8000 Hz. However, the NXT cannot play tones above 11,500 Hz, so you will not be able to test frequencies above this point.
3. The students will probably be able to find people of middle age or older who are unable to hear the highest tones.
4. This activity leads to considerable glee among the students as they find that some teachers cannot detect sounds that are perfectly audible to the students.
5. Of course, it is important to conduct this activity in a way that does not embarrass anyone or make anyone feel awkward. One way of avoiding problems is to solicit adult volunteers ahead of time.

Sample Program for Hearing Test

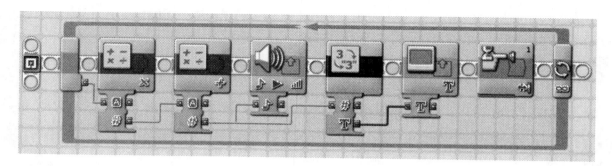

First Math block:

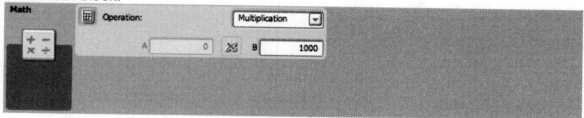

Second Math block:

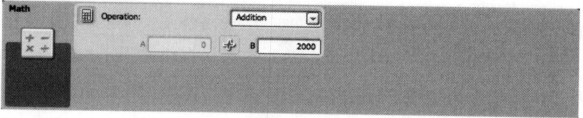

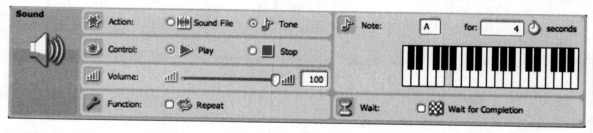

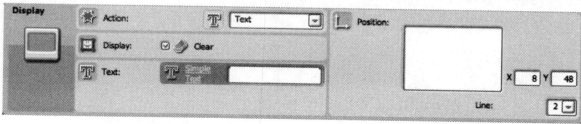

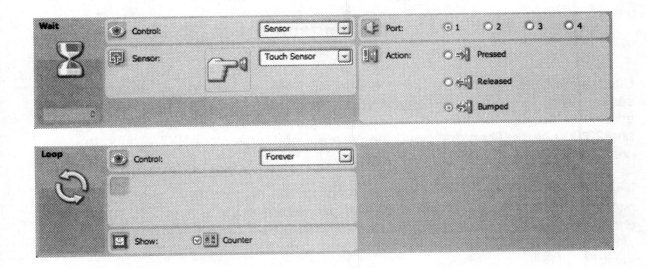

Answers to Hearing Test

1. Answers will vary.
2. Answers will vary. Some of the students will probably find older adults who cannot hear the highest tones.
3. Answers will vary. In general, the ability to hear high frequencies decreases with age.

Musical Instrument

Build a musical instrument using either the light sensor or the ultrasonic sensor. Write a program to convert your sensor readings into tones that are audible to people; the human ear can detect frequencies between about 20 and 20,000 hertz. Then download the program and move your NXT around to create a song.

If you choose to use the light sensor, program the instrument to play higher pitches when the light is bright and lower pitches when the light is dim. If you choose the ultrasonic sensor, program the instrument to play higher pitches when the sensor is close to an object and lower pitches when it is farther away.

To write the program, you will employ data hubs, using the output from the sensor to determine the tone frequency of the Sound block. However, remember that the frequencies detected by the human ear (20-20,000 hertz) are generally much larger numbers than the sensor output. You will need to use the Math block to adjust the sensor output before wiring it to the tone frequency plug of the Sound block.

1. What operation do you think would work best for the Math block? Addition, subtraction, multiplication, division? What number would you choose to add, subtract, multiply, or divide by? (Remember that the light sensor reads values between 1 and 100 and the ultrasonic sensor reads values between 1 and 200.)

2. As an added complication, your NXT internal speaker is able to produce tones between approximately 200 and 12,000 hertz. Knowing this, modify your conversion factor if necessary. What conversion factor do you plan to use? What range of tone frequencies will it produce?

Download and run your program. Experiment with varying the duration of the note and the conversion factor. See which combination sounds best.

    3. What note duration did you choose?

    4. What conversion factor did you decide upon?

Extension: Turn your instrument into a trombone, with a sliding piece that changes the pitch of the sound.

Teacher Information   Musical Instrument

In this activity, the students use light or ultrasonic sensors to create music by programming the NXT to convert sensor readings to musical tones.

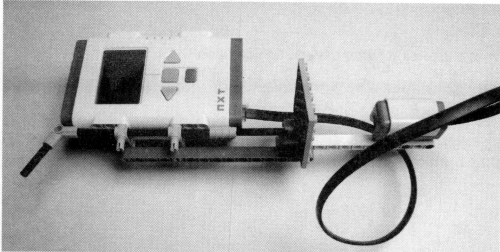

This musical instrument has a sliding piece that changes the pitch by altering the light-sensor readings.

Objectives
1. To experiment with changes in pitch and duration.
2. To write a program that uses sensor output to control another process.

Materials
NXT
Computer
Light sensor or ultrasonic sensor
LEGO® pieces

Time: Approximately 40 minutes

Notes
1. The program required for this activity is fairly sophisticated, making use of data hubs and the Math block. The students should be familiar with both before starting this activity. Applause Meter, in the Projects section, is a good activity to do before this one; the program is similar but does not include a Math block.
2. If you wish to have your students experiment with pitch without writing the program, you can give them the program and have them experiment with changing the duration of the note and the conversion factor from sensor reading to hertz.

Sample Program for Musical Instrument

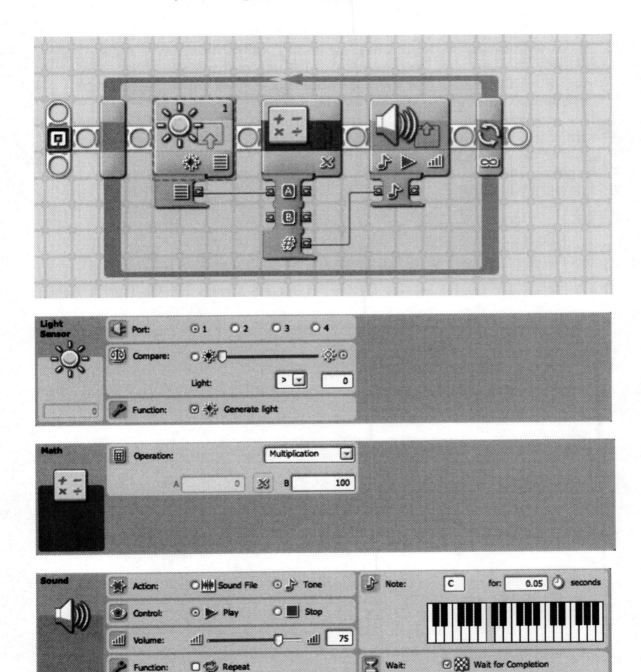

This program multiplies the value of the light-sensor reading by 100 to convert it into a reasonable value for hertz. This value in hertz is played for 0.05 seconds. The program then repeats.

Answers to Musical Instrument

1. To vary the sound depending upon the value read by a sensor, multiply the value of the sensor output using the Math block. The multiplier should be between 20 and 200 for the light sensor and between 20 and 100 for the ultrasonic sensor.
2. The students may adjust the conversion factor to put the values within the range of the NXT internal speaker. Not all of the values need to be within the range.
3. Answers will vary.
4. Answers will vary.

Acknowledgement

This activity is based upon one by Professor Chris Rogers of Tufts University.

Ultrasonic Pendulum

Turn your NXT into a pendulum. To do this, suspend the NXT from a pair of strings, with the ultrasonic sensor anchored to the NXT and pointed down towards the floor. You will need to build a frame to hold the ultrasonic sensor against the NXT. Your contraption will have to be balanced so that the ultrasonic sensor is perpendicular to the floor, rather than hanging at an angle.

Once you have built your pendulum device, write a data-logging program to log the ultrasonic sensor 20 times per second for ten seconds. Download the program to your NXT.

Suspend the pendulum device from the overhead support. Pull back the NXT, start the program running, and release the NXT. Let it swing back and forth for ten seconds.

Upload the data to the computer. It should look something like this:

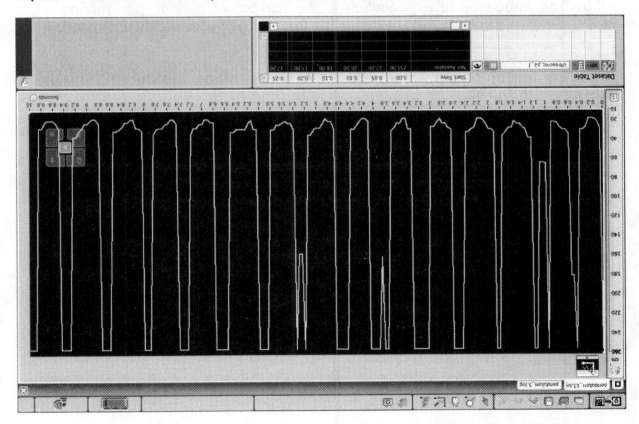

Identify a series of peaks on your graph that are fairly uniform. (For example, the second half of the graph above.) The time that a pendulum takes to complete one forward and back swing is called its period. Identify one complete period on your graph, starting from a minimum where the ultrasonic sensor was nearest the floor.

1. How many maxima (high points) are included in one period? What points in the pendulum's swing do they represent?

2. Identify three complete periods on your graph. How long did it take your pendulum to complete the three periods?

3. What is the period of your pendulum?

4. What is the advantage of averaging three swings to find the period rather than just using a single swing?

5. The frequency of a pendulum is the number of periods per second. It is measured in hertz (Hz). What is the frequency of your pendulum in hertz?

Does the length of the string affect the period of the pendulum? Design an experiment to find out.

6. Describe your procedure:

7. Make a data table to record your results:

8. What conclusion(s) can you reach based upon your data?

Teacher Information   Ultrasonic Pendulum

The students use ultrasonic sensors to investigate pendulum periods.

The ultrasonic sensor is used to find the period of the pendulum by logging the distance from the NXT bob to the ground.

Objectives
1. To design a frame for the ultrasonic sensor so that it can be used as a pendulum bob.
2. To use data logging to log the ultrasonic sensor.
3. To find the period and frequency of a pendulum.
4. To investigate whether the length of the string affects the period of the pendulum.

Materials
NXT
Computer
Ultrasonic sensor

LEGO® parts
String
Ring stand or other support for the pendulum
Meter stick

Time: Approximately 60 minutes

Notes
1. The pendulum bob can be rigged a number of different ways. The important considerations are that the ultrasonic sensor is facing downward and that the pendulum swings without twisting.
2. Ring stands make good supports for the pendulum, since their heights can be easily adjusted for the string-length experiment.
3. Assuming that the angle at which a pendulum is released is relatively small, the period of the pendulum is governed by the relationship

$$T = 2\pi (L / g)^{1/2}$$

where T is the period of the pendulum
L is the length of the string
g is the acceleration due to gravity.

Sample Program for Ultrasonic Pendulum

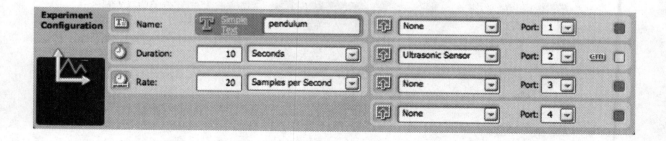

Answers to Ultrasonic Pendulum

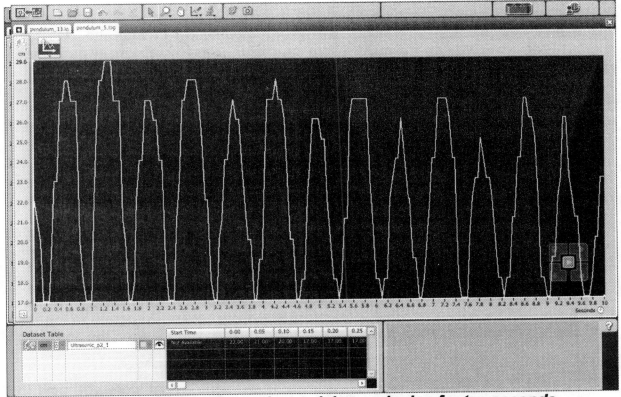

Sample data for an ultrasonic pendulum swinging for ten seconds.

1. There are two maxima in each pendulum period, one representing the swing to the right and the other the swing to the left.
2. Answers will vary. For the sample graph above, three periods took about 4.4 seconds.
4. Answers will vary. For the sample graph above, the period is about 1.5 seconds.
5. Taking the average of three periods gives you a larger data set and helps to reduce the effect of measurement error.
6. Answers will vary. The frequency of the sample pendulum is approximately 0.67 Hz.
7. Answers will vary. The students should test their pendulum with different length strings, attempting to keep all of the other variables constant.
8. Answers will vary.
9. Answers will vary. In general, the students should find that lengthening the string increases the period of the pendulum. The data will not be precise enough to allow them to find a quantitative relationship, but they should be able to discern a qualitative one.

Bright Light

The NXT motor converts electrical energy to mechanical energy. In this activity, we will reverse this process, converting the motor's mechanical energy into electrical energy. That is, we will turn the motor into a generator, using the electricity generated to light a lamp.

Attach a lamp brick to a motor using a converter cable. Attach a tire to the motor and run it along the ground.

1. What happens?

How bright a light can you produce with your generator? Design additions to your generator and lamp to make the light as bright as possible. You may attach a crank to the motor and a reflector to the lamp brick.

Construct your bright-light maker. Once you are satisfied with your design, you will test it using a light sensor located 20 centimeters away. Write a program to log the light sensor as you run your device. Test your device and answer the following questions.

2. Based upon your light-sensor readings, how bright a light were you able to generate?

3. Sketch and describe your design.

Teacher Information   Bright Light

The students use the NXT motor as a generator. They then design cranks and reflectors to produce as bright a light as possible, using data logging to gauge the effectiveness of their designs..

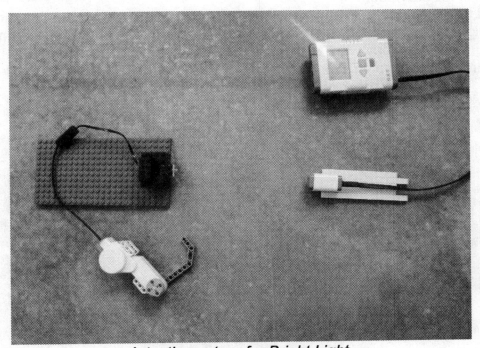

A testing set-up for Bright Light.

Objectives
1. To use a motor as a generator.
2. To design an effective crank.
3. To design a parabolic reflector.
4. To use the data-logging program to measure design performance.

Materials
NXT
Computer
Motor
Light sensor
Lamp brick
LEGO® pieces
Aluminum foil
Meter stick

Time: Approximately 50 minutes

Notes

1. You will need a dark area for testing the cranks and reflectors. The room does not need to be pitch-black. You may want to have a single testing station for the class so that the results of the various designs can be meaningfully compared.
2. The lamp brick should be placed 20 cm from the light sensor. Construct a holder for the lamp brick out of LEGO® bricks so that it is held at a uniform height and distance for each test.
3. To aid the students in constructing reflectors, you may want to show them headlights or other parabolic reflectors. Depending upon their mathematical background, you may want to discuss the mathematics of parabolas.
4. Constructing the cranks can be used to discuss torque or wheels and axles.

Sample Program for Bright Light

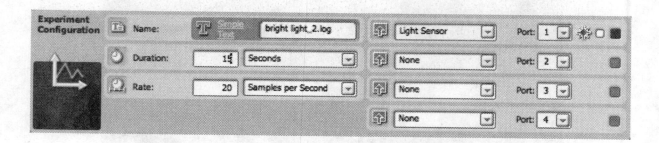

Answers to Bright Light

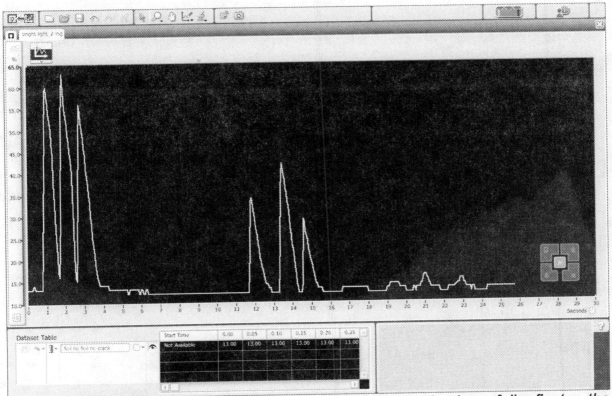

The first set of peaks was produced using a crank and aluminum-foil reflector, the second set using a crank but no reflector, and the third (very small) set using neither a crank nor a reflector.

1. The lamp brick lights.
2. Answers will vary.
3. Answers will vary. The most effective designs will generally include both a crank and a reflector.

Part Eight: Mostly Mathematics Activities

All of the activities in this section are focused on mathematical concepts.

The activities in this section are:
1. Random or Not?
2. Voting Machine
3. Do You Have a Sister?
4. Reaction Time
5. Which Room?
6. Grassfire
7. Logic Gates

Random or Not explores the concept of randomness. Voting Machine, Do You Have a Sister, and Which Room concern probability. Reaction Time looks at data analysis, including maxima, minima, and means. Grassfire introduces the idea of an algorithm. Logic Gates serves as an introduction to Boolean algebra.

A robot takes light–sensor data in Which Room.

Random or Not

Some of the NXTs have been programmed to display a random sequence of numbers. In others, the sequence of numbers is not random. Can you figure out which is which?

A random NXT
• is equally likely to display 1, 2, 3, 4, 5, or 6 each time
• does not follow any sort of repeating pattern
• has each number independent of the ones that came before.

Try each NXT and note your results below. To test an NXT, start the program running and press the touch sensor. Each time you press the sensor, you will hear a tone and see a number on the display screen. Generate a sequence of numbers and try to decide if the NXT is random or not.

Report the results of each run as a string of numbers. For example, the string 1332… would mean that the first time you pressed the touch sensor, the NXT displayed the number one, the second time it showed a three, the third time it a three again, and the fourth time it showed a two. Test the NXT as many times as necessary to decide if the pattern is random or not. If you start a new run, indicate it with a slash. Good luck!

Label color:

Results:

Random or not?

If not, why not?

Label color:

Results:

Random or not?

If not, why not?

Label color:

Results:

Random or not?

If not, why not?

Label color:

Results:

Random or not?

If not, why not?

Label color:

Results:

Random or not?

If not, why not?

Label color:

Results:

Random or not?

If not, why not?

Label color:

Results:

Random or not?

If not, why not?

Teacher Information

Random or Not

In this activity, the students use the NXT to investigate randomness.

Objectives
1. To explore the concept of randomness.
2. To investigate how sample size can influence the conclusions drawn.

Materials
Several NXTs
Touch sensors
Computer
Labels of different colors

Time: Approximately 40 minutes

Notes
1. Before starting this activity, program each NXT. Some bricks should contain the random program; the others should each contain one of the non-random programs outlined below. Mark each NXT with a different color of label.
2. Encourage the students to sample a long enough sequence of numbers that they are able to reach reliable conclusions.
3. The sequence of random numbers 1 through 6 appears to be fairly random. However, if the program is changed to generate random numbers from 1 through 4, it no longer appears to be random. Instead, it generates long sequences of alternating numbers. For example, here is one sequence of seventy-four (supposedly) random numbers: 31313131414141414141414141432323414141414 1414141432323414141414143232323232323. As an extension, you may want to give this version of the program to the students and let them test it for randomness. This test can lead to a discussion of randomness—which conditions of randomness are met by the numbers generated by this program--and also to a discussion of the difficulties involved in having a computer generate a truly random sequence of numbers.

Sample Programs for Random or Not

Random—this program generates a random sequence of the numbers 1 through 6:

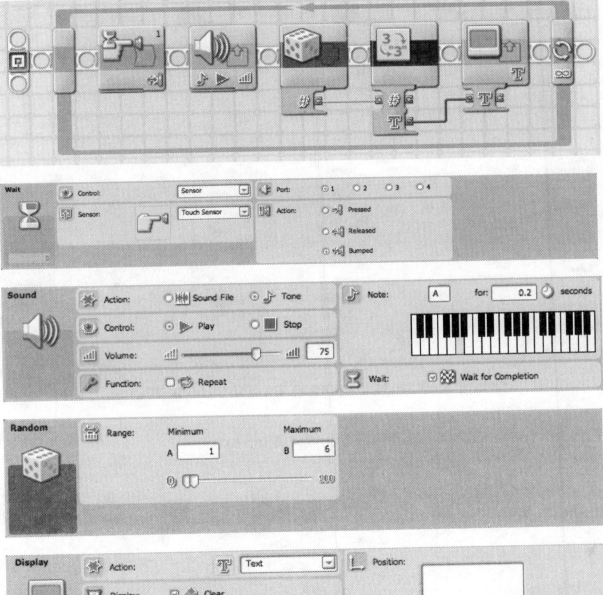

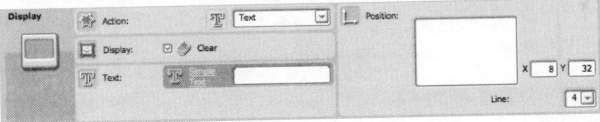

Repeating sequence 1, 2, 3, 4, 5, 6:

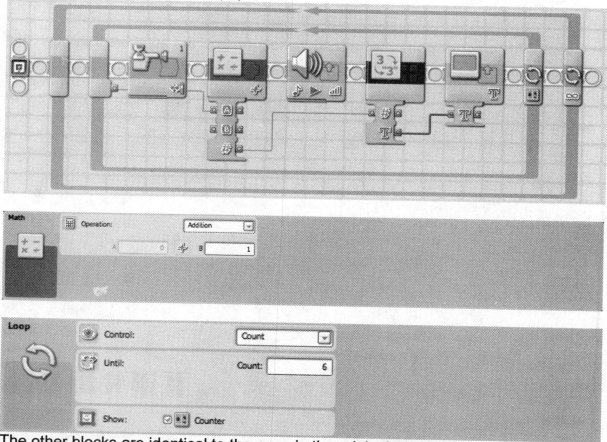

The other blocks are identical to the ones in the original program.

Random sequence of the numbers 1, 2, 3, 4, 5 (no 6):

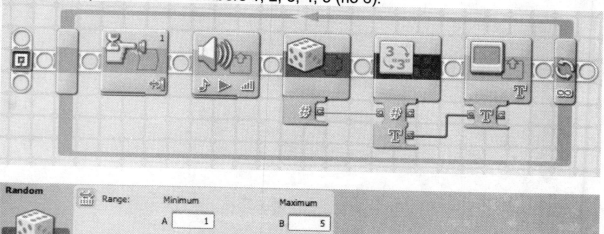

The other blocks are identical to the ones in the original program.

Repeating sequence of a random number followed by the next consecutive number:

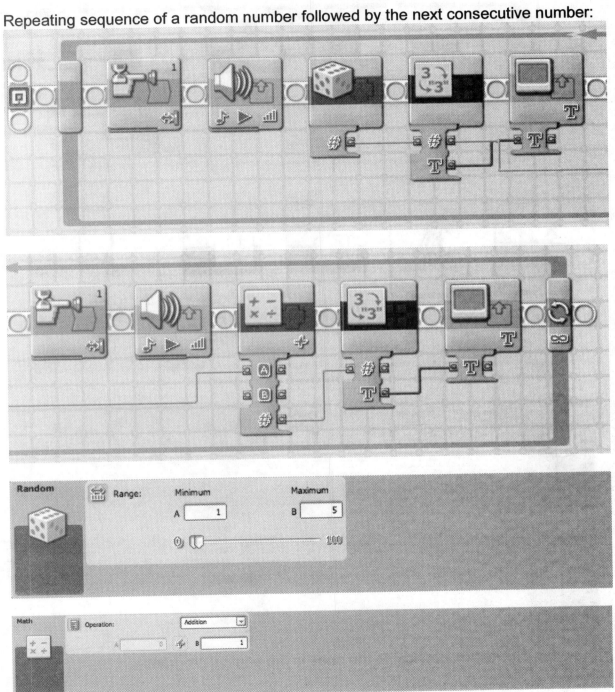

The other blocks are identical to the ones in the original program.

Alternating sequence of a random number and the number 2:

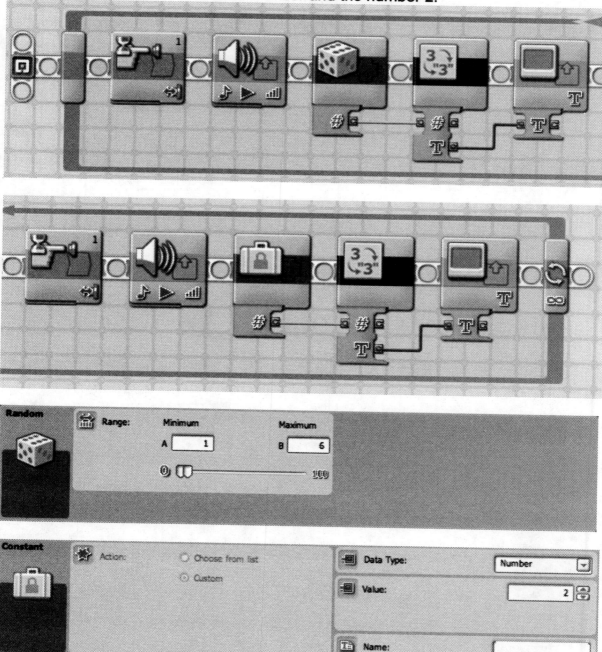

The other blocks are identical to the ones in the original program.

Voting Machine

A well-designed and accurate voting machine is of vital importance. Build a voting machine using two touch sensors, and then use it to poll your classmates on a question of your choice.

The program will tally the number of times two touch sensors are pressed, one in port 1 and the other in port 3, and display the results on the screen. The program will run indefinitely; when you have finished collecting the votes, write down the totals and press the dark gray button to abort the program. Before you end the program, make sure that you note the number of votes—the numbers will disappear when you end the program.

Choose the question you want your classmates to answer. Be sure to choose one with two clear answers, such as a yes/no question or one where the voter chooses between two options. Write the question on a card and label the two touch sensors.

The program is written to display a "yes" tally for touch sensor one and a "no" tally for touch sensor two. If your question is not a yes/no question, you can modify the display by changing the text in the Text blocks at the beginning of the program.

Once your machine is ready, have your classmates vote. (Be sure to start the program running before you begin.)

Teacher Information   Voting Machine

In this activity, the students use an NXT voting machine to collect votes.

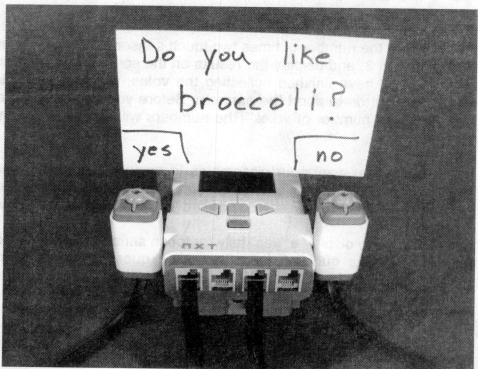

A machine ready for voting.

Objectives
1. To log two sensors at once to record votes.
2. To consider some of the issues of voting-machine design and use.

Materials
NXT
Computer
Two touch sensors
LEGO® pieces
Cards and labels

Time: Approximately 30 minutes, if the program is given to the students

Notes
1. The voting machine can be very simple—the NXT with two touch sensors attached—or more elaborate, with levers to pull.
2. The voting-machine program is rather advanced, making use of loops running in parallel and multiple data hubs. Unless your students are proficient at programming, you may want to provide it for them.

Sample Program for Voting Machine

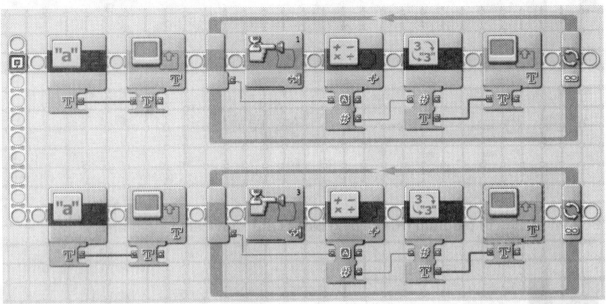

Top branch of program:

Text

"a"	Text:	A	Yes
		B	
		C	

Display

	Action:	Text	Position:	
	Display: ☐ Clear			
	Text: Sample Text		X 8 Y 56
			Line: 1

Wait

	Control:	Sensor	Port: ⦿ 1 ○ 2 ○ 3 ○ 4
	Sensor:	Touch Sensor	Action: ○ Pressed
			○ Released
			⦿ Bumped

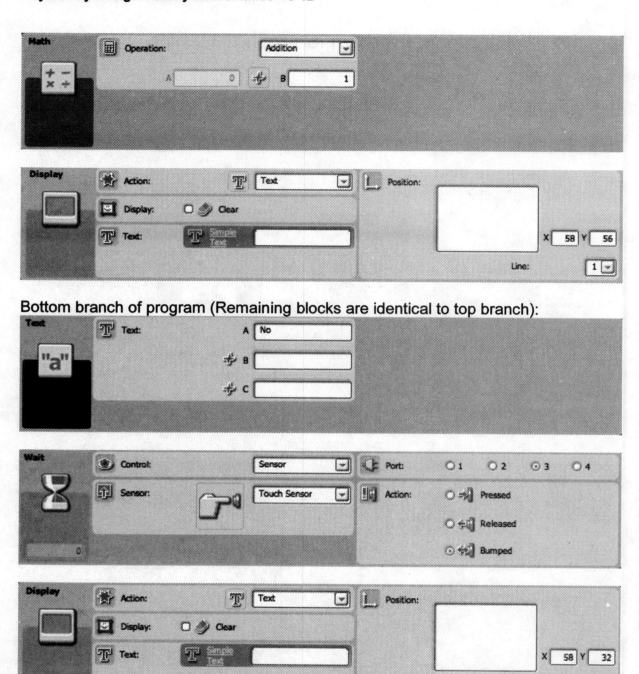

Bottom branch of program (Remaining blocks are identical to top branch):

Do You Have a Sister?

If you ask people if they have a sister, who is more likely to answer yes, males or females? We will run an experiment to find out.

1. First, make a prediction. Do you think more males will answer yes than females, more females than males, or do you think the numbers will be roughly equal?

We will poll a large number of people about whether they have a sister. To collect the data, we will need two voting machines for each group of people we poll, one for males and one for females.

Build two machines with two touch sensors on each. Attach a card containing the question to each machine and clearly label the touch sensors YES and NO. Also be sure to label one machine Males and the other Females to help ensure that the voters use the correct machines.

The program will tally the number of times two touch sensors are pressed, one in port 1 and the other in port 3, and display the results on the screen. The program will run indefinitely; when you have finished collecting the votes, write down the totals and press the dark gray button to abort the program. Before you end the program, make sure that you note the number of votes in each category—the numbers will disappear when you end the program.

Use your machines to poll a group of people.

2. Once your poll is complete, record your findings in the data table below. Record the data from the other groups as well.

Group polled	# of girls with sisters	# of girls total	% of girls with sisters	# of boys with sisters	# of boys total	% of boys with sisters
Total						

3. What do your data show? Are males or females more likely to have sisters?

4. Do you think this result is true in general? Justify your answer.

Teacher Information   Do You Have a Sister?

In this activity, the students use voting machines to collect data to answer a question about probability.

The voting results are displayed on the screen. Axles can be added to the touch sensors of the NXT to make push buttons for voting.

Objectives
1. To collect large amounts of data in an organized fashion.
2. To solve a probability problem.

Materials
NXT
Computer
Two touch sensors
LEGO® pieces
Cards and labels

Time: Approximately 60 minutes

Notes
1. The voting-machine program is rather advanced, making use of loops running in parallel and multiple data hubs. Unless your students are proficient at programming, you may want to provide it for them.

Sample Program for Do You Have a Sister?

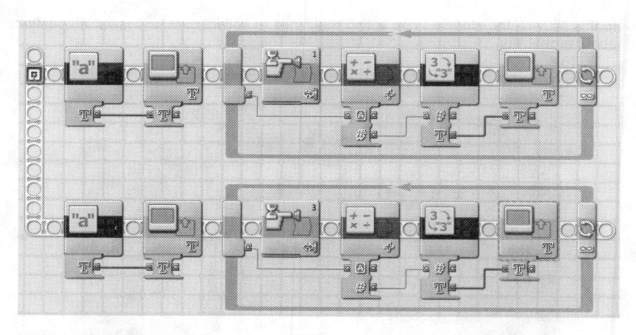

Top branch of program:

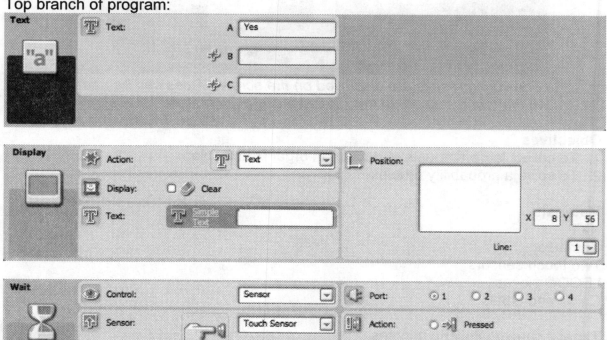

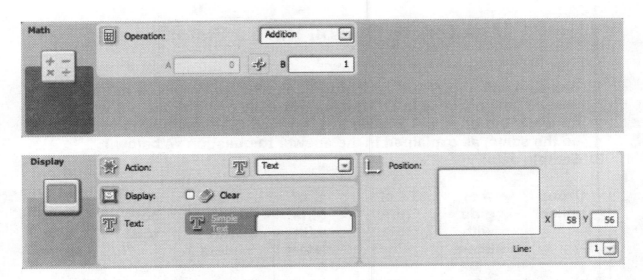

Bottom branch of program (Remaining blocks are identical to top branch):

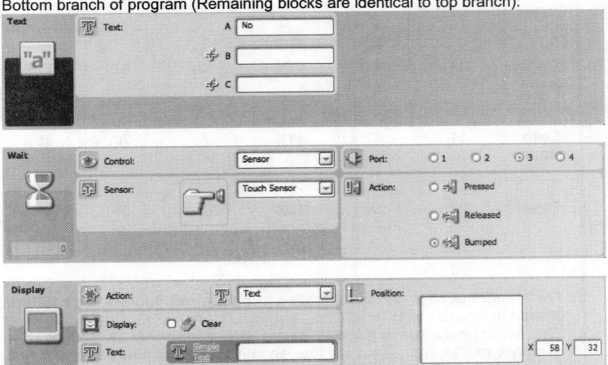

Answers to Do You Have a Sister?

1. Answers will vary. Many students think that males will be more likely to answer yes, because in all families with only one girl, the girl will answer no while the boys will answer yes. (In fact, the numbers on average will be the same, as explained in the answer to question #4 below.)
2. Sample data:

Group polled	# of girls with sisters	# of girls total	% of girls with sisters	# of boys with sisters	# of boys total	% of boys with sisters
Kinder-Garten	6	15	40%	4	13	31%
Third grade	11	16	69%	12	17	71%
Sixth grade	11	27	41%	7	20	35%
Total	28	58	48%	23	50	46%

3. For large data sets, the percentages of males and females with sisters should be about equal.
4. This result holds true in general. To see why, think about all families with exactly two children. There are four equally likely possibilities: two boys, two girls, an older boy and younger girl, and an older girl and younger boy. In the two-boy families, both boys will answer no. In the two-girl families, both girls will answer yes. In the mixed-sex families, the girls will answer no and the boys will answer yes. So, of these eight types of children, half the girls will answer yes and so will half the boys. This line of reasoning holds true for families with more than two children as well.

Reaction Time

How fast can you react to a stimulus? Use the NXT to measure your reaction time.

Attach a lamp brick to port A and a touch sensor to port 1. When the reaction-time program is run, the lamp will turn on after a random interval. As soon as it lights up, press the touch sensor as quickly as you can. The program will record how long you took to react in milliseconds and display the result.

Run the program five times, making sure to write down your reaction time at the end of each run.

1. What was your fastest time for the light-stimulus program?

2. What was your slowest time for the light-stimulus program?

3. Calculate your average reaction time for the light-stimulus program. What was it?

Do your react as quickly to a stimulus you hear as to one you see? To find out, modify the program to play a sound instead of turning on a light. Be sure to uncheck the Wait for Completion box of the Sound block so that the timer starts as soon as the sound begins. Run the program and compare your results to the light-stimulus version.

4. What was your fastest time for the sound-stimulus program?

5. Your slowest time for the sound-stimulus program?

6. Your average time for the sound-stimulus program?

Does a distraction affect your reaction time? To find out, modify the light-stimulus program to flash a second lamp brick on and off while you wait for the first lamp brick to light.

7. What was your fastest time for the distraction test?

8. Your slowest time for the distraction test?

9. Your average time for the distraction test?

Look back at your three sets of data.

10. Does the type of stimulus (light or sound) appear to make a difference?

11. Does the presence of a distraction appear to make a difference?

Teacher Information   Reaction Time

The students use data logging to investigate reaction time.

Objectives
1. To use data-logging to measure reaction time.
2. To examine the mean, minimum, and maximum of a data set.
3. To see what factors affect reaction time.

Materials
NXT
Computer
Touch sensor
Lamp bricks

Time: Approximately 40 minutes

Notes
1. The reaction-time program is too complicated for most students to write by themselves. You can give the light-stimulus program to the students and have them modify it for the other parts of the activity. Modifying the existing program should be straightforward for any student who is proficient at programming. Alternatively, the teacher can write the modifications ahead of time and the students can download them as needed.

Answers to Reaction Time

1-9. Answers will vary
10. Answers will vary, though most students should find only small differences between the two stimuli.
11. Answers will vary. Many students will find that the presence of a second light increases their reaction times.

Sample programs for Reaction Time

Reaction Time Light-Stimulus Program:

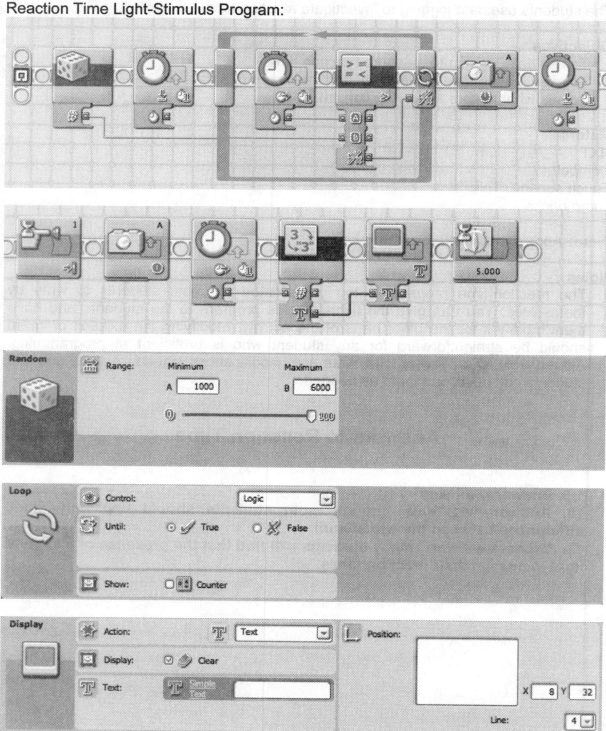

Reaction Time Sound-Stimulus Program:

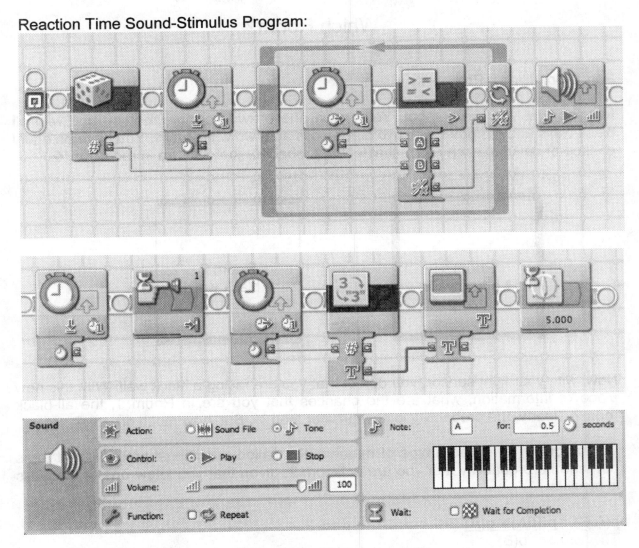

All other blocks are the same as in the preceding program.

Reaction Time Light-Stimulus Program with Distraction:

Add the following branch to the light-stimulus program.

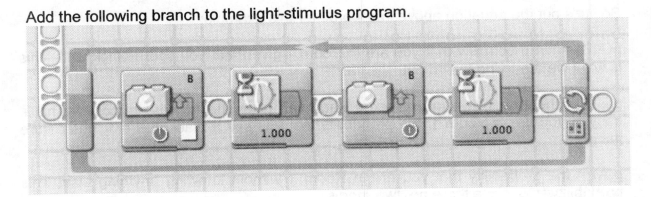

Which Room?

Part I: Conditional Probability

Imagine that you are a robot. You are in one of two possible rooms—one with all black walls and the other with two black walls and two white walls. You have an equal chance of being in each room; that is, the probability that you are in room 1 = ½.

Room 1
4 black walls

Room 2
2 black walls

Now, with your light sensor, you detect that you are facing a black wall. With this new piece of information, what are the chances that you are in Room 1, the all-black room? Clearly, the probability is now greater than ½. But, how much greater?

To find out, we will use a type of mathematics called conditional probability. It turns out that the probability that you are in Room 2, given that you know one of the walls is black is

$$p(A|B) = \frac{p(B|A) \times p(A)}{p(B)}.$$

where A = you are in Room 1
B = you see a black wall
p() = the probability that the event in parentheses occurs.

So, let's put the equation above into words for this example:

p(A|B) = the probability that you are in Room 1 given that you see a black wall—this is what we are trying to find out.

p(B|A) = the probability that you see a black wall, given that you are in room 1. This is easy: if you are in Room 1, the probability that you see a black wall = 1. It is a sure thing!

p(A) = the probability that you are in Room 1 without knowing anything else. This probability = ½, since there are two rooms.

p(B) = the probability that you will see a black wall. Since there are a total of eight walls and six of them are black, p(B) =6 out of 8 or ¾.

So, $p(A|B) = \dfrac{p(B|A) \times p(A)}{p(B)} = \dfrac{1 \times ½}{¾} = \dfrac{4}{6}$ or $\dfrac{2}{3}$.

1. How many black walls would you need to see to be absolutely sure (p = 1) that you are in Room 1 instead of Room 2?

Suppose we add a third room. Room 3 has three black walls and one white wall. Again, the robot detects a black wall.

Room 3
3 black walls

2. Now what are the chances that the robot is in room 1? Are your chances better, worse, or the same as in the two-room situation? Show your work.

Part II: The Mystery Room

Now, you are ready to try your robot. Your robot will be placed in one of the four rooms shown below. You will be allowed to take five seconds of light-sensor readings while standing still.

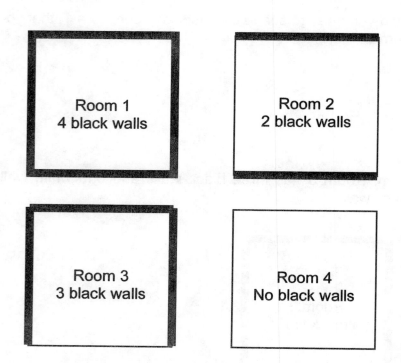

Room 1
4 black walls

Room 2
2 black walls

Room 3
3 black walls

Room 4
No black walls

Write a program to collect the data. Before trying your program in the mystery box, use the test box to calibrate your sensor so that you know what light-sensor readings correspond to black walls and white walls.

3. Black wall reading in test box _____

4. White wall reading in test box _____

Give your NXT to the teacher, who will run your program in the mystery box and return the car to you.

5. Light-sensor reading in mystery box _____

6. Most likely color of wall _____

How many black walls is the mystery room most likely to have? To find out, calculate the conditional probability for Rooms 1-4 based upon your light-sensor reading. Show your work below.

7. Conditional probability that Room 1 is the mystery room:

8. Conditional probability that Room 2 is the mystery room:

9. Conditional probability that Room 3 is the mystery room:

10. Conditional probability that Room 4 is the mystery room:

Of course, usually a robot can take more than one reading in order to determine which room it is in. Suppose that you have fifteen seconds to take readings in the mystery room. What strategy would you use?

Write a program to collect light-sensor data in the mystery box. You may move around inside the box and take as many readings as you like, but your program may only run for fifteen seconds.

11. Write a brief description of your program:

12. Describe the data you collected:

13. What do you think the inside of the mystery box looked like?

14. How confident are you of your results? Explain.

Teacher Information

Which Room?

The students investigate conditional probability using Bayes' Rule.

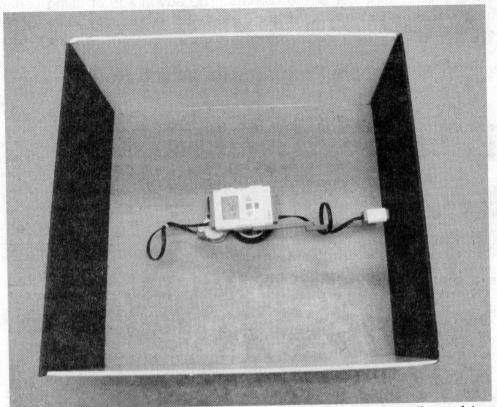

A robot takes data in Room 2, which has two black walls and two white walls.

Objectives
1. To apply Bayes' rule to solve a few simple discrete-probability problems.
2. To program a robot to collect light-sensor data.
3. To design a plan for determining which of four rooms the robot is in.

Materials
NXT
Computer
Light Sensor
LEGO® pieces
Rooms with black and white walls

Time: Approximately 90 minutes

Notes
1. The students will need to know some very basic probability before beginning this lab. However, they do not need to know any conditional probability beforehand.
2. The mystery rooms can be constructed out of sheets of stiff black and white cardboard taped together at the corners. The advantage of using separate walls is that the number of black and white walls in each room can be easily changed.

Sample Programs for Which Room

Program to take five seconds of light-sensor data in the mystery room:

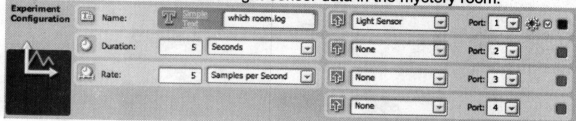

Program to take 15 seconds of data while moving:

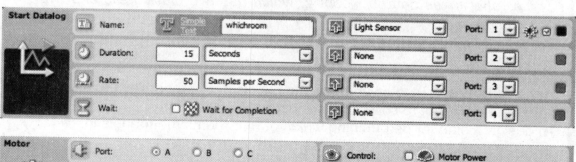

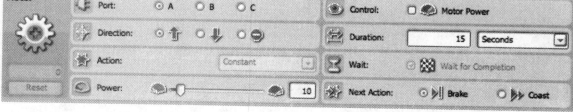

Answers to Which Room?

Part I: Conditional Probability

1. You would need to see three black walls. As soon as you see more that two walls, you can be certain that you are not in Room 2, since it only has two black walls.

2. $p(A|B) = \dfrac{p(B|A) \times p(A)}{p(B)} = \dfrac{1 \times 1/3}{9/12} = \dfrac{4}{9}$

Your chances of being in Room 1 are lower.

Part II: The Mystery Room

3. Answers will vary.

4. Answers will vary.

5. Answers will vary.

6. Answers will vary.

7. Conditional probability that Room 1 is the mystery room if your light-sensor reading indicated a black wall:

$p(A|B) = \dfrac{p(B|A) \times p(A)}{p(B)} = \dfrac{1 \times 1/4}{9/16} = \dfrac{4}{9}$

If your light-sensor reading indicated a white wall:

$p(A|B) = \dfrac{p(B|A) \times p(A)}{p(B)} = \dfrac{0 \times 1/4}{7/16} = 0.$

8. Conditional probability that Room 2 is the mystery room if your light-sensor reading indicated a black wall:

$p(A|B) = \dfrac{p(B|A) \times p(A)}{p(B)} = \dfrac{1/2 \times 1/4}{9/16} = \dfrac{2}{9}$

If your light-sensor reading indicated a white wall:

$p(A|B) = \dfrac{p(B|A) \times p(A)}{p(B)} = \dfrac{1/2 \times 1/4}{7/16} = \dfrac{2}{7}$

9. Conditional probability that Room 3 is the mystery room if your light-sensor reading indicated a black wall:

$p(A|B) = \dfrac{p(B|A) \times p(A)}{p(B)} = \dfrac{3/4 \times 1/4}{9/16} = \dfrac{1}{3}$

If your light-sensor reading indicated a white wall:

$p(A|B) = \dfrac{p(B|A) \times p(A)}{p(B)} = \dfrac{1/4 \times 1/4}{7/16} = \dfrac{1}{7}$

10. Conditional probability that Room 4 is the mystery room if your light-sensor reading indicated a black wall:

$p(A|B) = \dfrac{p(B|A) \times p(A)}{p(B)} = \dfrac{0 \times 1/4}{9/16} = 0.$

If your light-sensor reading indicated a white wall:

$p(A|B) = \dfrac{p(B|A) \times p(A)}{p(B)} = \dfrac{1 \times 1/4}{7/16} = \dfrac{4}{7}$

11. Answers will vary. The students may collect as many readings as possible while rotating the robot to see multiple walls. Alternatively, they may program the robot to turn exactly 360 degrees while collecting readings.

12. Answers will vary.

13. Answers will vary depending upon the configuration of the mystery box and the quality of the students' data.

14. The students should not be expected to be able to generate the conditional probability of multiple events. However, they should have a general sense of how compelling (or not) their data are.

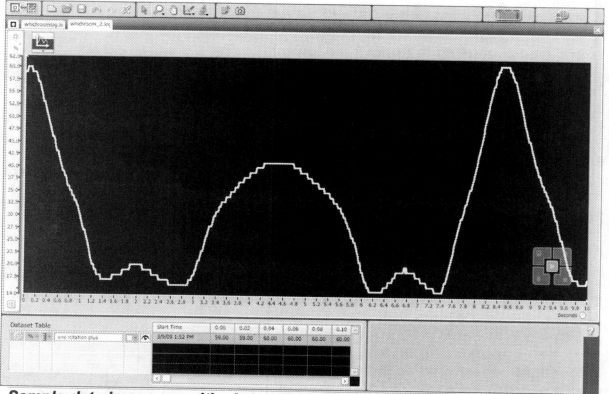

Sample data in a room with alternating black and white walls. The light sensor is mounted on a long arm, causing a peak whenever the sensor is closest to each wall—a larger peak for a white wall and a smaller peak for a black one.

Grassfire

Part I: The Theory

A robot cannot plan the same way a person can. Instead, it must have a particular set of rules to follow in order to develop a plan. For example, look at the map below. Suppose that the robot knows where it is and also knows where the goal is--it has a map of some sort. The robot needs a specific set of rules, an algorithm, for planning a route around the obstacle and reaching the goal.

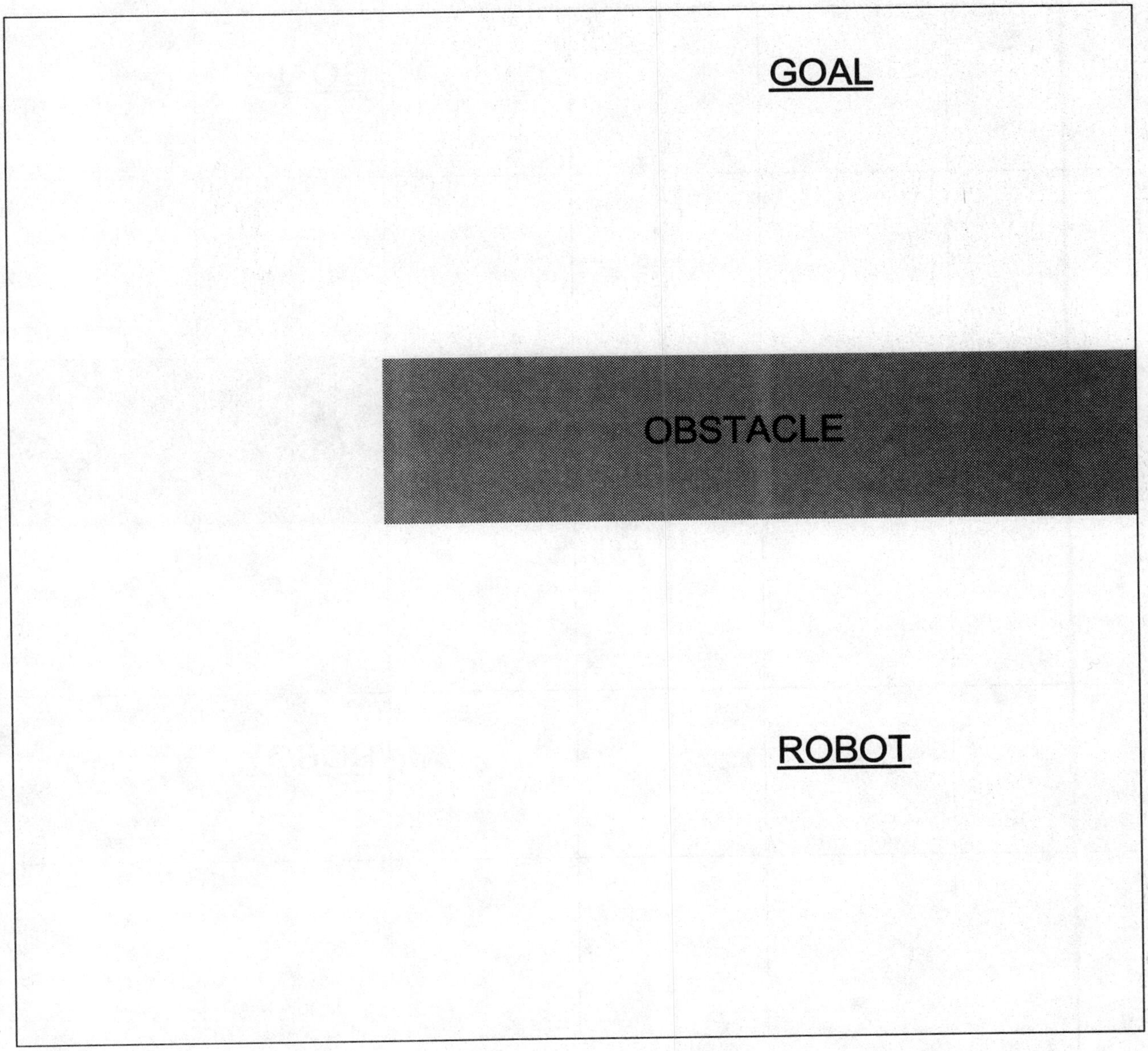

GOAL

OBSTACLE

ROBOT

One commonly used algorithm is called the NF1, or grassfire, algorithm. Here's how it works: The map is divided into equal boxes, or cells. The cell containing the goal is given a value of zero. Every cell that is adjacent to the zero box, either horizontally or vertically (but not diagonally), is given a value of one. Every cell adjacent to a one box is given a value of two, and so on, until the entire grid is filled. As the grid is being filled, boxes containing obstacles are skipped.

1. Use the grassfire algorithm to fill in the grid below.

				GOAL	
		OBSTACLE		OBSTACLE	OBSTACLE
				ROBOT	

Once the grid is filled in, the robot is ready to plan its path. It needs a set of rules for this step also. The rule that the robot uses in the grassfire algorithm is to begin at the robot's starting cell and look for the adjacent cell with the lowest number. For this part of the algorithm, the robot can look at diagonally adjacent cells as well as horizontal and vertical ones. It can also skip numbers. For example, if the robot is in a ten box and has both a nine box and an eight box adjacent to it, it can move directly to the eight box. The robot moves to the adjacent cell with the lowest number and then repeats the process, moving to successively lower numbers until it reaches zero, the goal.

2. On the map you numbered earlier, use the grassfire algorithm to draw the robot's path to the goal.

3. Was the robot able to reach the goal?

4. How did the path you drew using the algorithm compare to the shortest possible path?

5. Suppose that we changed the algorithm to say that you could not skip numbers as you traced the path. In other words, if the robot were in a ten box and had both a nine box and an eight box adjacent to it, it could not move directly to the eight box. It would have to move to the nine box first and then to the eight box. How would this change affect the robot's path?

Of course, it is possible to vary the size of the cells in the grid. The first grid was six cells across and six cells down. Below is the same map, but this time the grid is only three cells by three cells.

6. Use the grassfire algorithm to number the cells and then draw the robot's path. If a cell has a part of an obstacle in it, you may not enter that cell, even if the obstacle does not cover the whole cell.

7. Was the robot able to reach the goal using the three-by-three grid?

8. How did its path compare with the shortest possible path?

9. Name two possible advantages of using a grid with big cells (like the three-by-three grid) over using a grid with smaller cells (like the six-by-six grid).

10. Name two possible disadvantages of using a grid with big cells over using a grid with small cells.

Part II: The Robot

Now that you have seen how the grassfire algorithm works, let's try a simple implementation of it. To do so, you will string together a series of command blocks: Drive straight between cells, Drive diagonally between cells, Turn left 45 degrees, Turn right 45 degrees, Turn left 90 degrees, and Turn right 90 degrees.

Before you can use these blocks to control your robot, you will need to adjust the milliseconds (thousandths of a second) needed to drive straight and to turn 45 degrees, since these times will vary from robot to robot.

Open the grassfire program. You should see a program that looks like this:

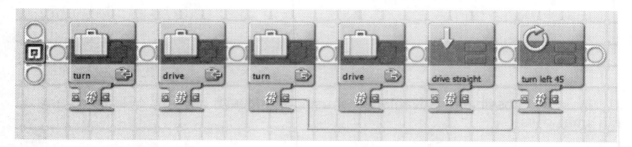

Making your best guess, input the number of milliseconds your robot must turn in order to rotate 45 degrees into the Variable block named "turn." Do the same for the time needed to cross one cell of the grid, entering the value into the Variable block named "drive." Then, download and run the program to test your values. Adjust them as necessary.

Once you are satisfied with your distance and angle values, you are ready to build your program. Add blocks to the grassfire program to form the sequence your robot will use to traverse the obstacle course. You will find the blocks in the My Blocks section.

After your program is complete, place your robot in the starting position of the obstacle course and run the program.

11. How did your robot do on the obstacle course? What are some of the shortcomings of this simple building-block program?

Teacher Information   Grassfire

The students investigate the NF1, or grassfire, algorithm for path planning.

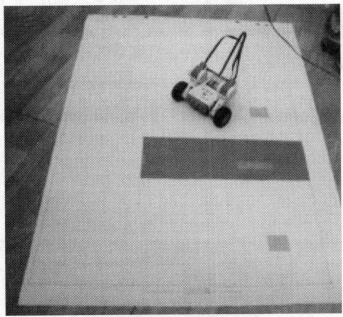

A simple obstacle course.

Objectives
1. To apply the grassfire algorithm to a map to navigate past an obstacle and reach a goal.
2. To investigate the effects of the fineness of the grid chosen.

Materials
Computer
NXT car
Large paper with grid for making the obstacle course

Time: Approximately 80 minutes

Notes
1. Part II of this activity may be done in two ways. One possibility is to have the students write their own custom blocks for Turn Left 45 degrees, Drive Straight, etc. The other possibility is to provide the programs and have the students change the inputs to match their particular car. The sample blocks are shown below. As written, they require just two inputs: the number of milliseconds needed to turn the car 45 degrees and the number of milliseconds needed to drive the length of one grid square. Once these two inputs are entered, the program calculates all of the other values needed.

2. Depending upon the orientation of the motors on each car, the direction arrows on the custom blocks may need to be reversed.
3. After completing this introduction, the students can try more complicated maps or try designing their own.
4. Some questions to discuss with the students: If a path to the goal exists, will the grassfire algorithm always find it? (Yes, unless the cell size is large enough that narrow openings are in the same cell as obstacles and thus disappear off the map.) In the case of multiple paths along the grid, will the algorithm always choose the shortest one? (Yes.)
5. The command-block program will allow the students to try the grassfire algorithm, though it is too simple a program to be very accurate, especially for finer grids or more complicated obstacle courses.

Sample Programs for Grassfire

Grassfire (main program for testing values and calling the Custom Blocks below):

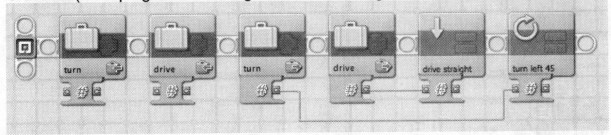

Turn left 45 degrees block:

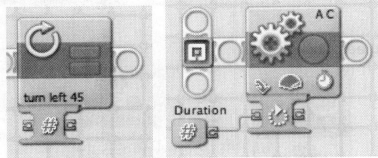

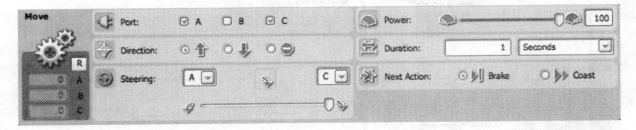

Turn left 90 degrees block:

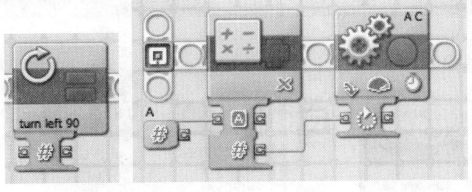

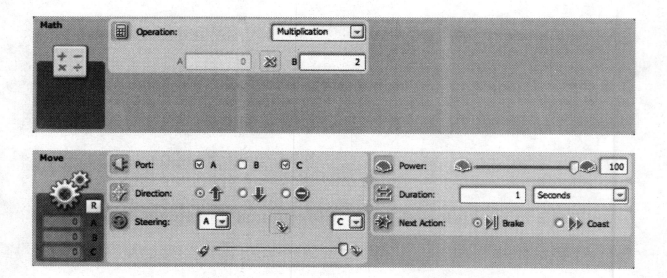

Turn right 45 degrees block:

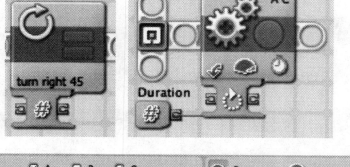

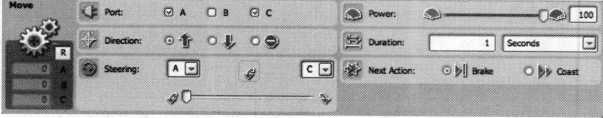

Turn right 90 degrees block:

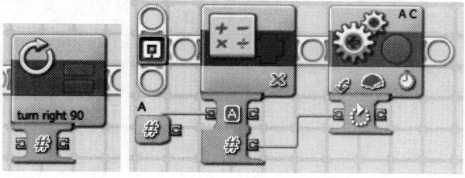

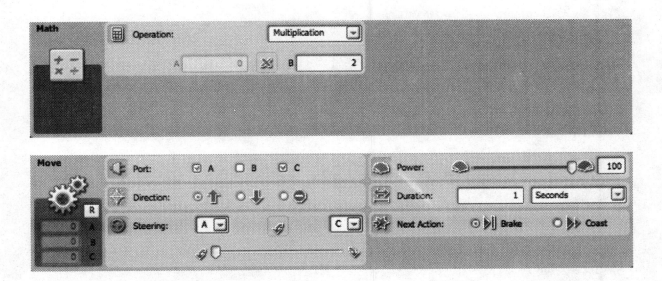

Drive straight across one cell block:

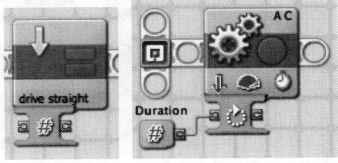

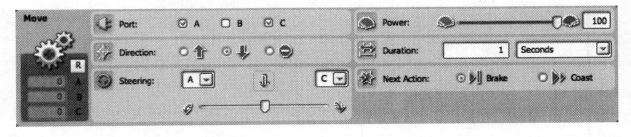

Drive diagonally across one cell block:

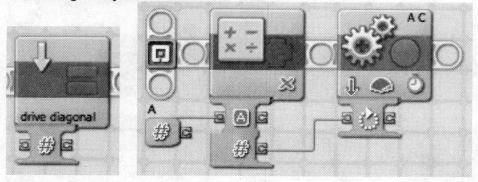

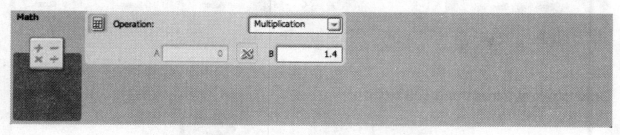

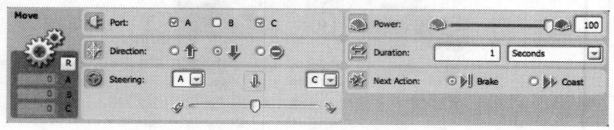

Answers to Grassfire

1. The completed grid:

4	3	2	1	0 **GOAL**	1
5	4	3	2	1	2
6	5	OBSTACLE			
7	6	7	8	9	10
8	7	8	9	10 **ROBOT**	11
9	8	9	10	11	12

2. The robot's path using the grassfire algorithm:

		2	1		
4	3			0 **GOAL**	1
5	4	3	2	1	2
6	5		OBSTACLE		
7	6	7 / 8		9	10
8	7	8	9	10 **ROBOT**	11
9	8	9	10	11	12

3. **Yes, the robot was able to reach the goal.**
4. **The path is close to the shortest possible, except for some added distance to reach the center of each cell.**
5. **The path would no longer contain diagonal shortcuts, so its total distance would be greater.**

6. Three-by-three grid with values shown:

		GOAL
2	1	0
3	OBSTACLE	
		ROBOT
4	5	6

Three-by-three grid with robot's path shown:

7. Yes, the robot was able to reach the goal using the three-by-three grid.
8. Longer, because the new path gave the obstacle a wider berth on one side because of the coarseness of the grid.
9. Possible advantages of using a grid with big cells over using a grid with smaller cells:
   ● Fewer steps are needed to assign values to all of the cells and to trace the path.
   ● A coarser grid takes less computer memory to store.
   ● The larger cells mean that the robot's path is often further from the edges of obstacles, so it is less likely to collide with them.

10. Possible disadvantages of using a grid with big cells over using a grid with small cells:
    - It is difficult to model complicated fields containing multiple obstacles with a coarse grid.
    - The robot may travel further than necessary because it has a wider margin around obstacles.
    - Narrow openings may disappear if they are in the same cell as an obstacle.
    - If the goal is much smaller than the cell, the robot may finish in the correct cell, but still not reach the goal.

11. Answers will vary. A major problem with the building-block program is that the robot does not check the accuracy of its position along the way, so that small errors accumulate. Another problem is that the diagonaldrive and turn90degrees blocks are just scaled versions of the straightdrive and turn45degrees blocks, and scaling may not be accurate in this situation.

Sample Program for Navigating the Grassfire Course

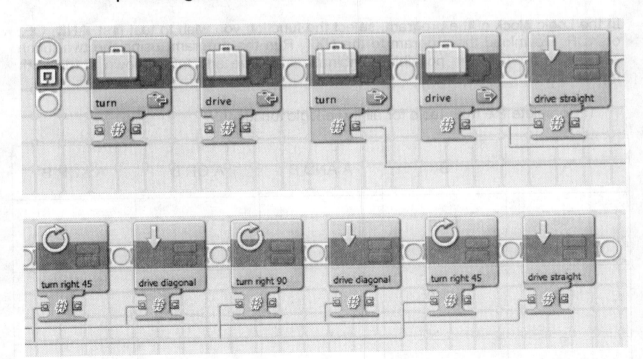

Logic Gates

Logic gates are used in designing circuits. Three common ones are AND, OR, and XOR. The Logic block in NXT Mindstorms contains all three. In this activity, you will simulate the different types of logic gates using the Mindstorms software.

Plug one touch sensor into port 1 to represent statement A. Plug the second touch sensor into port 3 to represent statement B. Plug a lamp brick into port A to represent the logic function you are testing.

The logic-gates program turns the lamp brick on if the condition is true and off if it is false. For example, let's say you want to test A AND B when A is true and B is false. You hold down the touch sensor in port 1, representing A, but not the touch sensor in port 3, representing B. Then you check the lamp brick. It is off, meaning that A AND B is false when A is true but B is false. The program repeats over and over, allowing you to test all of the combinations of true and false by pressing the various combinations of the two touch sensors.

In the Logic block of the program, select the function you wish to test first, AND, OR, or XOR. Download the program to the NXT. Run the program, using the two touch sensors to produce the possible combinations of true and false shown in the truth table below.

1. Complete the truth table for all three logic functions:

A	B	A AND B	A OR B	A XOR B
True	True			
True	False			
False	True			
False	False			

You will see that there is a fourth option for the Logic block, NOT. NOT acts upon a single variable, negating it. In other words, if A is true, then NOT A is false. If A is false, then NOT A is true.

2. Modify the logic-gates program so that the following values are produced:

A	B	Result
True	True	False
True	False	True
False	True	True
False	False	True

What change(s) did you need to make?

Teacher Information

Logic Gates

The students investigate logic gates.

Objectives
1. To program using Logic blocks.
2. To use truth tables.
3. To investigate the logic gates AND, OR, XOR, NOT, and NAND.

Materials
Computer
NXT
Touch sensors
Lamp brick

Time: Approximately 40 minutes

Notes
1. The program required for this activity is fairly sophisticated. To do this activity, give the students the basic logic-gates program and have them modify it as they complete the handout.
2. You may want to demonstrate one combination to show the students how to use the program.
3. As an extension, challenge the students to create a NOR gate, in which a true value is returned if and only if both A and B are false. As the name implies, this can be done by combining an OR gate and a NOT gate.

Sample Program for Logic Gates

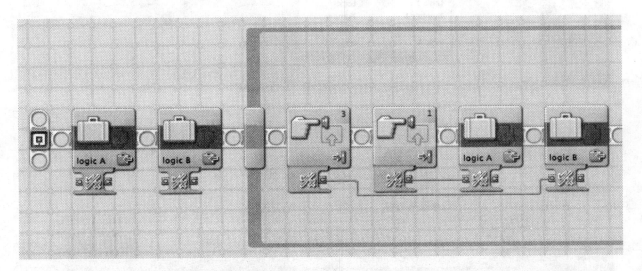

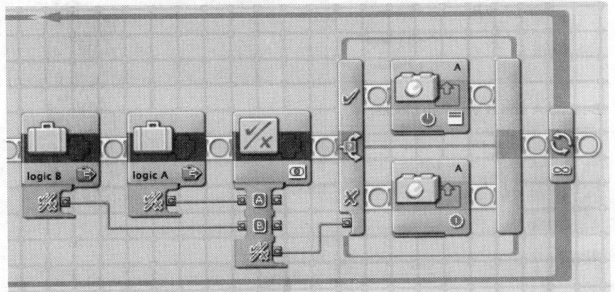

First A and B Variable blocks:

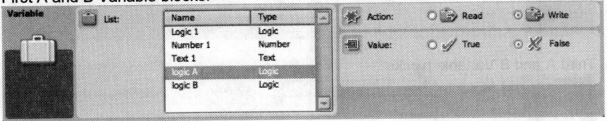

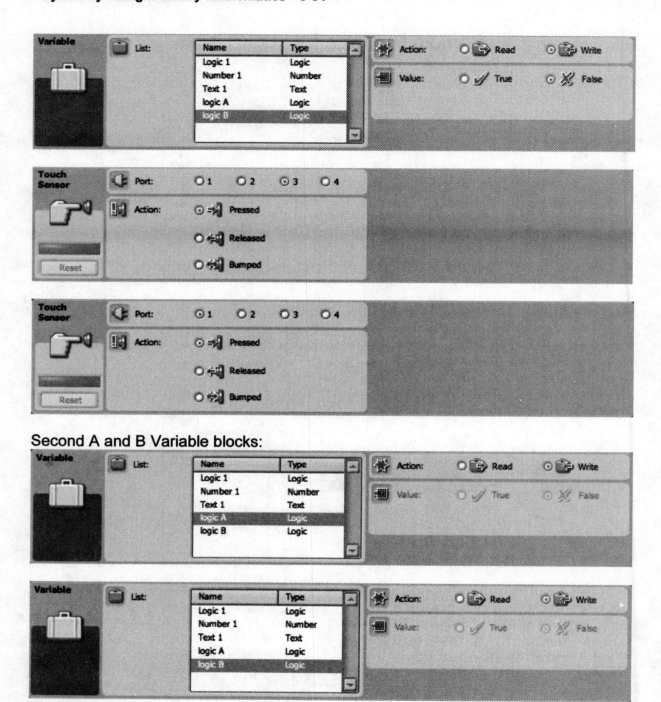

Second A and B Variable blocks:

Third A and B Variable blocks:

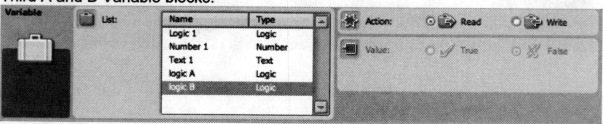

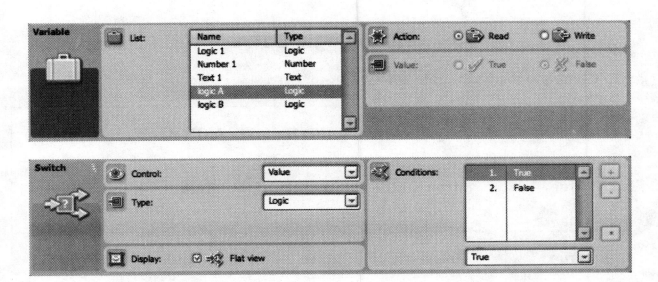

Answers to Logic Gates

1. **Complete the truth table below:**

A	B	A AND B	A OR B	A XOR B
True	True	True	True	False
True	False	False	True	True
False	True	False	True	True
False	False	False	False	False

2. **The truth table describes a NAND (NOT AND) gate. To create it, modify the AND program by adding a NOT Logic block after the AND Logic block.**

Appendix A: Alignment with the National Science Education Standards for the United States

The physics and data-logging activities in this book are aligned with the National Science Educational Standards for the United States, developed by the National Committee on Science Education Standards and Assessment of the National Research Council in 1996. The standards summarize the understandings and abilities needed to be scientifically literate at each grade level, K-12.

In addition to outlining science content for each age group, the standards present a broader philosophy of science education, based upon the premise that science is an active process and that learning it must be an active process also. According to the standards, inquiry should be central to science learning, with students actively engaged in combining scientific knowledge with logical and critical thinking.

Engineering can be a powerful and exciting way to engage students in the process of science and in scientific thinking. In addition to meeting these broad goals, the activities in the physics section address many of the specific content standards. The tables on the following pages summarize the content standards for grades 5-8 and 9-12. For each physics and data-logging activity in the book, the standards addressed by that activity are indicated by X's in the corresponding boxes of the grid.

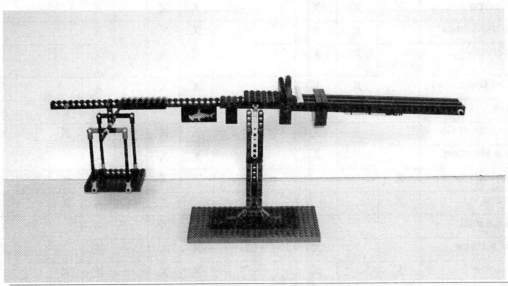

A LEGO double-beam balance.

Alignment with the National Science Standards, Grades 5-8

Content Standards

Activities	Understanding, abilities aligned with systems, order, and organization	Understanding, abilities aligned with evidence, models, and explanation	Understanding, abilities aligned with constancy, change, and measurement	Understanding, abilities aligned with evolution and equilibrium	Understanding, abilities aligned with form and function	Abilities necessary to do scientific inquiry	Understandings about scientific inquiry	Properties and changes of properties in matter	Motions and forces	Energy and transfer of energy	Structure and function in living systems	Abilities of technological design	Understandings about science and technology
Getting Up to Speed	X	X	X			X	X		X				X
Stop for Pedestrians	X	X	X			X	X		X			X	X
Parking Space	X	X	X			X	X		X				X
Crossing the Lines		X	X			X	X		X				X
Spinning your Wheels		X	X			X	X		X				X
Zigzag and Diamond		X	X			X	X		X				X
No Wheels			X		X				X			X	X
Action-Reaction Car			X		X	X	X		X	X		X	X
Bricks in a Newton			X			X	X		X				X
Gear Training	X						X		X	X			X
Worm Gears	X						X		X	X			X
Spinning Colors							X				X	X	X
At a Snail's Pace			X			X	X		X			X	X
Perfect Pitcher	X		X			X	X		X	X			X
Pulley Systems	X	X	X		X				X	X			X
Ramp Up		X	X			X	X		X	X		X	X
Peak Performance		X	X			X	X		X	X		X	X
Balancing Nails		X			X	X	X		X				

Activities	Understanding, abilities aligned with systems, order, and organization	Understanding, abilities aligned with evidence, models, and explanation	Understanding, abilities aligned with constancy, change, and measurement	Understanding, abilities aligned with evolution and equilibrium	Understanding, abilities aligned with form and function	Abilities necessary to do scientific inquiry	Understandings about scientific inquiry	Properties and changes of properties in matter	Motions and forces	Energy and transfer of energy	Structure and function in living systems	Abilities of technological design	Understandings about science and technology
Tightrope Walker				X	X	X			X			X	X
LEGO Balance				X	X	X	X		X			X	X
Building Pressure			X						X				
Floating LEGO Bricks		X	X			X		X	X				
Cartesian Diver	X	X	X			X	X	X	X				
Stir It Up	X	X	X			X	X		X	X			X
It's a Breeze	X	X	X			X	X		X	X			X
Cool It Fast	X	X	X		X	X	X		X	X		X	X
Hearing Test			X		X					X	X		
Musical Instrument			X							X		X	X
Ultrasonic Pendulum		X	X			X	X		X	X		X	X
Bright Light		X	X		X	X			X	X		X	X
Light and Dark Scavenger Hunt		X	X										X
I'm Thinking of a Number		X	X			X							X
Thunderstorm		X	X			X			X				X
Melting		X	X			X	X		X				X
Cave Explorer		X	X			X			X				X

Alignment with the National Science Standards, Grades 9-12

Content Standards

Activities	Understanding, abilities aligned with systems, order, and organization	Understanding, abilities aligned with evidence, models, and explanation	Understanding, abilities aligned with constancy, change, and measurement	Understanding, abilities aligned with evolution and equilibrium	Understanding, abilities aligned with form and function	Abilities necessary to do scientific inquiry	Understandings about scientific inquiry	Motions and forces	Conservation of energy and increase in disorder	Interactions of energy and matter	The behavior of organisms	Abilities of technological design	Understandings about science and technology
Getting Up to Speed	X	X	X			X	X	X					X
Stop for Pedestrians	X	X	X			X	X	X				X	X
Parking Space	X	X	X			X	X	X				X	X
Crossing the Lines		X	X			X	X	X					X
Spinning your Wheels		X	X			X	X	X					X
Zigzag and Diamond		X	X			X	X	X					X
No Wheels			X		X			X				X	X
Action-Reaction Car			X		X	X	X	X				X	X
Bricks in a Newton			X			X	X	X					X
Gear Training	X						X	X					X
Worm Gears	X						X	X					X
Spinning Colors							X				X	X	X
At a Snail's Pace			X			X	X	X				X	X
Perfect Pitcher	X		X			X	X	X					X
Pulley Systems	X	X	X		X			X					X
Ramp Up		X	X			X	X	X	X			X	X
Peak Performance		X	X			X	X	X	X			X	X
Balancing Nails		X		X		X	X	X					

Activities	Understanding, abilities aligned with systems, order, and organization	Understanding, abilities aligned with evidence, models, and explanation	Understanding, abilities aligned with constancy, change, and measurement	Understanding, abilities aligned with evolution and equilibrium	Understanding, abilities aligned with form and function	Abilities necessary to do scientific inquiry	Understandings about scientific inquiry	Motions and forces	Conservation of energy and increase in disorder	Interactions of energy and matter	The behavior of organisms	Abilities of technological design	Understandings about science and technology
Tightrope Walker				X	X		X	X				X	X
LEGO Balance				X	X	X	X	X				X	X
Building Pressure			X					X					
Floating LEGO Bricks		X	X			X		X					
Cartesian Diver	X	X	X			X	X	X					
Stir It Up	X	X	X			X	X	X	X				X
It's a Breeze	X	X	X			X	X	X	X				X
Cool It Fast	X	X	X		X	X	X	X	X			X	X
Hearing Test			X			X				X	X		
Musical Instrument			X							X		X	X
Bright Light		X	X			X	X	X		X		X	X
Ultrasonic Pendulum		X	X					X	X			X	X
Light and Dark Scavenger Hunt		X	X										X
I'm Thinking of a Number		X	X			X							X
Thunderstorm		X	X			X				X			X
Melting		X	X			X				X			X
Cave Explorer		X	X			X				X			X

Appendix B: Activities Listed by Topic

Velocity
    Getting Up to Speed 7-2
    Stop for Pedestrians 7-6
    Parking Space 7-9
    Crossing the Lines 7-12
    Spinning your Wheels 7-16
    Zigzag and Diamond 7-21
    No Wheels 7-27

Wheels and Axles
    Bright Light 7-120

Two girls test the accuracy of their pitching arm for Perfect Pitcher.

Appendix C: Mindstorms Equipment Used for Each Activity

	NXT	Motor	Lamp brick	Touch sensor	Light sensor	Rotation sensor	Ultrasonic sensor	Sound sensor	Temperature sensor
INTRODUCTORY:									
Build a Box	X								
Picture Box	X								
Simple NXT Cars	X	X							
COMMON PALETTE:									
Hello Goodbye	X								
Say Cheese	X							X	
Mimicry	X	X							
Snake	X	X							
Push-button Car	X	X		X					
Cloverleaf	X	X							
COMPLETE PALETTE:									
Clap On	X		X					X	
Daytime Fan	X	X			X				
Snail Trail	X								
Roll of the Die	X								
Three-Speed Fan	X	X			X				
Dog Years	X								
PROJECTS:									
Music Box	X	X							
Haunted House	X	X			X	X			
Meet and Greet	X	X	X	X	X				
Bug in a Box	X	X			X				
Outside the Box	X	X			X				

	NXT	Motor	Lamp	Touch sensor	Light sensor	Rotation sensor	Ultrasonic sensor	Sound sensor	Temperature sensor
Applause Meter	X	X						X	
Mini Golf	X	X	X	X	X	X	X	X	
Robotic Zoo	X	X		X	X	X	X	X	
Chain Reaction Machine	X	X		X	X	X	X	X	
EGGcellent Contraption	X	X		X	X	X	X	X	
Wacky Gumball Machine	X	X	X	X	X	X	X	X	
DATA LOGGING:									
Scavenger Hunt	X				X				
Thinking of a Number	X			X					
Thunderstorm	X				X			X	
Melting	X								X
Cave Explorer	X	X			X				X
PHYSICS:									
Getting Up to Speed	X	X							
Stop for Pedestrians	X	X							
Parking Space	X	X							
Crossing the Lines	X	X			X				
Spinning your Wheels	X	X				X			
Zigzag and Diamond	X	X				X			
No Wheels	X	X							
Action-Reaction Car									
Bricks in a Newton									
Gear Training									
Worm Gears									
Spinning Colors									

	NXT	Motor	Lamp	Touch sensor	Light sensor	Rotation sensor	Ultrasonic sensor	Sound sensor	Temperature sensor
At a Snail's Pace	X	X							
Perfect Pitcher	X	X		X					
Pulley Systems									
Ramp Up	X	X							
Peak Performance	X	X							
Balancing Nails									
Tightrope Walker									
LEGO Balance									
Building Pressure									
Floating LEGO Bricks									
Cartesian Diver									
Stir It Up	X	X							X
It's a Breeze	X								X
Cool It Fast	X	X							X
Hearing Test	X								
Musical Instrument	X				X		X		
Ultrasonic Pendulum	X						X		
Bright Light	X	X	X		X				
MOSTLY MATH:									
Random or Not	X			X					
Voting Machine	X			X					
Do You Have a Sister	X			X					
Reaction Time	X		X	X					
Which Room	X	X			X				
Grassfire	X	X							
Logic Gates	X		X	X					

	Temperature sense	Sound sense	Magnetic sense	Balance sense	Light sense	Touch sense	Push	Work	Tilt
Art & Shell 32-Pack								X	X
Perfect Pitcher						X		X	X
Pulley Systems									
Raise Up								X	X
Peak Performance								X	X
Balancing Balls									
Tightrope Walker									
LEGO Balance									
Building Pressure									
Floating LEGO bricks									
Series in Divers									
Stack Up	X						X	X	
It's a Breeze	X							X	
Crunch Test	X						X	X	
Heating Test								X	
Musical Instrument			X		X			X	
Unstructured Pendulum			X					X	
Bright Light					X		X	X	X
MOSTLY MATH									
Reason or Not					X			X	
Voting Machines					X			X	
Do You Have a Sister					X			X	
Reaction Time					X	X		X	
When Room Is					X		X	X	
Pressing								X	X
Logic Gates					X	X		X